The Toxic Metals

Pan/Ballantine

First published 1972
by Earth Island Limited, London.
This edition published 1972 by
Pan/Ballantine, 33 Tothill Street,
London S.W.1

Printed in Great Britain
by Richard Clay (The Chaucer Press), Ltd.,
Bungay, Suffolk

CONTENTS

Introduction—the danger all around   9

How death came to Minamata—a mystery investigated   15

Mercury strikes again—the sickness of Minamata spreads to Scandinavia, Canada and the United States   47

If mercury does not get you, lead probably will. Give us this day our daily lead   88

The metals you need, and the metals you do not want at any price—even if economists say they are good for you   138

Some looming threats: cadmium and nickel take to the air and no one was there to see   174

How public health authorities turn a blind eye yet pretend to protect you. The road to disaster   208

Glossary of terms   229

Index   233

References and notes have been given at the end of each chapter, not to create a spurious air of scholarship but to provide handles for those who want to start digging for themselves. The best available surveys of the scientific literature on mercury are *Mercury in the Environment— The Human Element* published in 1971 by the Oak Ridge National Laboratory, Tennessee, and *Methylmercury* by Dr Göran Löfroth, published in 1969 by the Swedish Natural Science Research Council. The Swedish authority has also published a short survey on the toxicity of cadmium, a study of lead in petrol and a collection of papers on metals and ecology. Two US publications are particularly useful for background information. *Mercury in the Environment* (US Geological Survey Professional Paper No 713) gives a very detailed account of the natural distribution of the metal, while the *Norton Nelson Report* (report by Dr Norton Nelson to the Secretary of the US Department of Health Education and Welfare 'Hazards of Mercury': Environmental Research: vol 4, pp 1–69, March 1971) reviews the Swedish findings and action of the late 'sixties. The scientific literature on other heavy metals in the environment is very thin, but a useful survey of the cadmium situation in the US appeared in the September 1971 issue of *Environment*.

INTRODUCTION

Heavy metals are among the most dangerous and least understood of contaminants. Because they exist naturally as part of the earth's crust they occur in all soils, rivers and oceans. In the right quantities some are essential to life. Others are so poisonous that only a few millionths of a gram can kill. Many that are capable of disrupting living processes are in widespread industrial use and, as contaminants, are extending through the biosphere, so that *in increasing quantities they distort the naturally occurring distribution of metals to form an accidental but potentially disastrous addition to the diet of all living things*.

Environmental attention in the recent past has tended to concentrate on pesticides, detergents and the more obvious aspects of air pollution, with the result that the heavy metals, in spite of their dangerous potential, have been largely overlooked. True, lead pollution has been a subject of controversy for many years, but the implications of mercury pollution, for example, broke on the world like a sudden disaster. Yet its history was long and the lessons of danger were there to be read many years before Western government or industry began to take serious action to limit its consequences.

When disaster finally came public reaction was violent and pock-marked with mis-statement and over-statement, so that official and industrial *defensive reaction* was both proper and inevitable. But this has led to a situation in which scientists, deeply concerned about the continuing and profligate contamination of the environment, are now worried because their message became garbled before it was properly understood. Wild reaction and well-meaning but vulnerable distortion have added a new facet to human blindness: the problems remain unresolved.

Vision is already dimmed by the commitment of Governments, industry and society to policies that, through the massive mobilization of natural resources, impose increasingly poisonous burdens upon essential living processes. With some activist environmental movements riding the crest of a wave of tactical success and now believing that, right or wrong, action can be rapid when necessary, the outlook is confused and far from cheering. *Vast man-mobilized doses of metallic poisons are being poured into the environment without any serious attempt to study their fate or effects.* No one has the slightest idea whether the present rates of mobilization and changes of metallic distribution are safe or not. New burdens of poisonous metals may, eventually, become overlaid or safely dissipated, but we have no knowledge of rates of change or of dissipation. The time-scale of change, once a local environment is poisoned, may be very slow. *By the time action appears necessary it is likely to be much too late.* Lakes taken out of commercial use a quarter of a century ago because of mercury contamination and, since then, unpolluted, remain unusable and poisonous to this day. Yet, with geneticist-apologists pointing out that all living organisms are designed to cope with changes, even the crucial driving ecological argument that mankind is blindly consuming and corrupting the hand that feeds him is being robbed of its force.

There are no genetic mechanisms capable of coping with sudden burdens of heavy metals, nor with gradually increasing chronic poisoning, just as there are no natural mechanisms to protect us against radiation, chemical mutagens or a dose of nerve gas.

The last half century has demonstrated all too clearly that biological adaptive processes are too *slow* to cope with the rate of environmental change induced by technology. Yet the alternative routes, those of savage, un-stabilizing, unnatural selection, or of chemically induced mutation which will certainly be regressive, can be re-garded as acceptable only by madmen. In the absence of adequate knowledge and at the present time the effects of man-induced metallic contamination are largely un-predictable—the only tolerable policy is one of extreme caution. Under the pressures of Western technocracy the thresholds of danger may long since have been crossed.

It is a sad reflection on the nature of humanity that scientists and technologists, ostensibly and often sincerely guarding our interests, can become blinkered by com-mitment to their own points of view. An industrial hygienist who has for years supported an industrial view—such as the innocuousness of vehicle exhaust lead in the atmosphere of cities—will defend his viewpoint to the last, especially if his work is largely supported by the polluting industry. And since, in the case of metal con-tamination as in the case of other low-level chemical contamination, the human whole-population effects are likely to be sub-clinical (that is, they do not reveal them-selves until there are significant changes in disease statistic) by then the damage is widespread and, perhaps for a group comprising several generations, may be entirely irreversible.

Professor Samuel Epstein of Harvard Medical School, perhaps unconsciously reiterating the warning voiced by the British geneticist Lionel Penrose back in the 'fifties, wrote in 1970 that there was

little doubt that many diseases hitherto regarded as spon-taneous are caused by environmental pollutants. This fear is heightened by the exponential increase in human exposure to new synthetic chemicals which, in general, are inadequately characterized toxicologically, quite apart from ecological effects.*

* 'Control of Chemical Pollutants', *Nature*: vol 228, p 816.

There is no doubt that, in his context, Professor Epstein is thinking primarily of the many new and often complex organic chemicals that are introduced into the environment each year without any serious attempt to determine their biological significance. Yet even in the case of *known* dangerous materials, like the heavy metals, incredibly little has been done to elucidate ecological or whole-population effects. *They seem somehow too familiar for concern until, in some dramatic and stupidly unnecessary incident, people and animals die.* The last quarter century has witnessed a series of unforgivable incidents of this kind which, in spite of their actual and implicit seriousness, have failed to hold the steady public and official attention needed for their prevention. And, if local disasters involving death do not prompt proper attention, what hope is there for the early detection and elucidation of underlying and insidious damage to man and the systems on which he depends for life?

It is indicative of disregard in the early 'seventies that the two most important general official documents on pollution in Britain—a White Paper produced by the Labour Government just before it was rejected from office, and the first annual report of the new Standing Royal Commission on the Environment—make only brief mention of heavy metal contamination and then in terms which suggest that the situation is not serious. This may be by no means a true reflection of the convictions of those involved with pollution studies behind the official front but, if that is so, then the implications are rather worse, for they include the possibility of deliberate official concealment. Through the establishment of monitoring systems the trend looks to be in the right direction but, if history is a guide (and we have no other), there are good reasons to worry.

Wilful forgetfulness seems to be a part of man's incurable optimism. The protective machinery of the Western world is geared primarily to the narrow homocentric point of view of general and industrial medicine.

The fear is that this narrow homo-centric point of view will couple with forgetfulness, Government disinterest and continued short-sighted economics, to ensure the continuation of so-called environment 'protection' systems which seem almost deliberately designed to ensure *disasters*, not security. Certainly the events of the past 20 years and the continual build-up of metal contamination of many kinds, reveal precisely that weakness. It is not simply that response is slow when it is urgently needed, but that it involves a kind of calculated duplicity in environmental *games* whose pawns are the general public and, ultimately, the whole fabric of life.

True, on many issues, Government and industry have to walk a kind of technical tightrope between sets of conflicting evidence, and have to weigh the economically practical against the environmentally desirable. But there are strong signs that all too often there is a tendency for official and industrial attitudes to lead towards interpretations that imply the least interference with the reigning political and industrial policy. Combined with scientific commitment, the result can be unconscious corruption which pervades and debases all argument.

The ultimate experiments, essential for the argument's resolution, are always carried out on us and on our supporting life forms. There is good reason to cavil. Yet this too has its dangers. Massive environmental protest, leading to abrupt technological change, demonstrably leads to the substitution of unknown for known devils. The ousting of phosphates for detergents, for example, looked a desirable thing during the battle but may have resulted in embracing a monster while rejecting a wolf. It now seems clear that the real battle should be against detergents *per se* and, since the doctrine of super-cleanliness is all pervasive even if based on advertising gimmickry rather than biological good sense, this is a battle in which it will take time even to make a convincing start.

That is, of course, an issue on its own, and the considerations of wild over-reaction do not in fact apply to heavy metal contamination. The necessity for change towards stringent control is conclusively demonstrable, without any need for expensive and extensive forward looks, and without the need to weigh the relative merits of differing courses of action. The ultimate biological costs are too high to waste time with arguments about the odd penny on the price of petrol. There are, to be sure, plenty of uncertainties in the technical arguments for those who seek either self-delusion or delay. But the heavy metals are *deadly*. If we can kill our lakes and rivers and watch the disease spreading to larger seas; if we can dumbly watch the rising blood-levels of children in spite of the possibility that this is putting their future mental capacity and stability in jeopardy; if we continue to pump materials into the environment which we know are capable of dramatic poisonous interference with biological processes that are absolutely fundamental to life and yet do nothing, then it is not systems, or Governments or industries which bear the final guilt. It is ourselves.

CHAPTER ONE

MAD CATS AND DEAD MEN
AT MINAMATA

Spring mellowed into dry summer. On Japan's southernmost island, Kyushu, peasant fishermen turned their eyes to the East China Sea and looked forward to the richest harvests of the year. To those of the West coast in and near Minamata, a town that is partly industrialized and partly an overgrown village, 1953 was neither harder nor more promising than usual. It became bizarre. As an almost unremarked prelude to disaster, the already ailing cats of Minamata, and of the coasts to the north and south, began to stagger, go mad and die.

As one by one with glazed eyes they moved, erratic and bewildered, towards coma and death, neither the peasant population among whom they died nor the public health authorities who early learned of these 'strange incidents' recognized the deadly mark of heavy metal poisoning. Men have always been slow to recognize the poisons in their environment, but at Minamata they were slower than usual. They paid a terrible price.

The dispersed nature of the fishing community and the semi-developed character of the town hindered official investigation and delayed the collation of events. According to the most detailed published record[1] the unknown but frightful paralytic disease that killed the cats struck the first human in December of the same year. It was the start of an eight-year epidemic during which, of a coastal population of 10,000, 43 were to die and a further 68, many of them infants and children, were to be permanently and grotesquely disabled. That is the official record. But the nature of the poisoning involved, organic mercury, is such that these numbers represent only the obvious tip of a much wider and more sinister pyramid of damage.

There can be little doubt that at that time the coastal population at large was suffering from widespread chronic mercury poisoning. Yet, *even when severe, chronic poisoning takes time to build up to the point at which overt and easily recognizable symptoms appear*. When at last, these *do* appear, they are not always recognized. That is what happened at Minamata. During the years that followed 1953 there was a rapid increase in the number of cases of adults and children suffering from a mysterious but severe loss of co-ordination, numbness of limbs, partial blindness and loss of hearing. Then they began to die, like the cats, through convulsions and coma. In 1954, of 12 cases, 5 died. Three of 15 died in 1955, and in 1956 there was an upsurge to 50 new cases. Of these 10 died, and 7 of them were infants born of mothers *who did not themselves show any signs of the disease*.

Until August 1956 the medical authorities, aware that they had something mysterious and appalling on their hands but unable to understand either its cause or pattern, believed that they might be dealing with some form of contagious brain inflammation. Patients, isolated as if with fever, failed to respond to treatment. Then, since the number of cases was rising at a rate sufficient to alarm even the most complacent, and because the proportion of deaths among infants and children was disturbingly large (40%), the medical centre at Minamata finally asked for help from the medical department at Kumamoto University some 50 miles away. It was already clear from the slow rate of recovery of those who did not die, and from the crippling disablement of those who made some kind of partial recovery, that this was a disease of unparalleled virulence.

THE CASEBOOK

Since it is all too easy to get involved with numbers and statistics in such a way that the real human implications become obscured, it is worth looking at a few case histories before delving into the investigation that finally identified their cause. In the course of the clinical study the cases were divided into *adult*, *child* and *foetal*, with each main division again subdivided into varying degrees of severity. Three case histories should, at this point, be enough to bring home the personal tragedies involved. The following are straightforward if simplified transcriptions taken directly from the Kumamoto medical records:

ADULT (case 2 in the records with initials M.F.). Woman aged 28, became ill on June 13 1956 with numbness in fingers and lips and with difficulty in hearing. By June 16 speech and ability to walk were markedly impaired, and she developed marked tremor of the hands accompanied by sometimes violent involuntary muscular convulsions. By early August she was unable to walk or to co-ordinate other movements; involuntary convulsions became more severe with outbursts of frenzied shouting and crying. After developing a high fever she was admitted to hospital on August 30. She was found to be severely emaciated and, suffering from involuntary seizures, unable to respond to normal stimuli, but shouting and screaming at intervals of about one minute. Her condition deteriorated rapidly. After a brief period of coma she died on September 2. The official final cause of death was pneumonia.

This case is typical of a group in which the patients died within 2 or 3 months of the onset of illness and which generally ended with the complication of pneumonia. It is described as the 'acute fulminant form' of the disease and all patients who suffered from it eventually died. The disease tended to be more dangerous in children among whom not only the acute fulminant form but also the chronic forms (that is to say the forms resulting from a lower intake of poison but over a longer period) were frequently fatal. Tragically in these cases the disease ran a much longer and more harrowing course.

> CHILD (case 11 in the records of infants and children: initials S.T.). Girl, born on November 24 1950 and first affected by the disease on March 31 1956 when, for one day, she developed a high fever. From that time onward she began to lose feeling and control in her hands and by April 13 was suffering from an impairment of speech. Four days later her ability to see began to diminish and she complained of difficulty in swallowing. Insomnia and extreme signs of nervousness followed and, since her general ability to control muscular movements was deteriorating, she was hospitalized on April 26. Convulsive seizures began shortly afterwards and it was necessary to force-feed her. After transfer to the specialist clinic on August 30 and treatment with detoxifying drugs, there was some temporary improvement. This was short-lived, and after a few days a general decline set in. By July 1957 she was suffering from generalized tremors with repeated convulsions, a condition which worsened to include involuntary laughing and crying by February 1968. By July 1968 she entered long periods of unconsciousness, with spasms, and on December 22, developed pneumonia. She died on January 2 1959, after almost 3 years of appalling suffering.

This child, whose sister was similarly affected but who made a partial recovery and is one of the many permanently disabled, came from a family in which, although on the same diet, the parents were unaffected. Although not realized at the time, this is now seen as one of several indications that *infants and growing children are far more sensitive to heavy metal poisoning than are adults*. This is a point to remember.

It is also the factor which underlies a third group of

Minamata disease victims—those who were affected either in the mother's womb or through ingestion of mercury by way of the mother's milk during the early stages of infancy. The notable thing in all these cases, of which 22 are recorded, is that all the mothers appeared to be normally healthy. The symptoms during the development of the children are somewhat different from those of adult or post-natal child poisoning, and in the most severe cases involved deformity, marked mental retardation and lack of muscular control, cerebral palsy and early death. In some ways the moderate cases were less lucky, for although some still survive they are permanently disabled.

CONGENITAL (case 8 in the records, moderately affected). Female, born on July 20 1956. Older sister died of Minamata disease in 1958 after showing first symptoms on June 30 1956. Neither parent showed symptoms and there was no history of hereditary disease. No abnormalities were noticed during pregnancy and birth, and the child had a normal weight and appearance. Yet at six months it became apparent that she had little muscular control. At 18 months she learned to sit up by herself, but she was 3 years old before learning to walk. Her gait was abnormal, tiptoed with arms outstretched, and so unsteady that she would fall after moving only a few feet.

She was first examined as a potential victim of congenital Minamata disease at the age 3 years and 5 months, at which time her ability to walk had not improved: she could recognize only a few words, and ate clumsily and only with a spoon. In general her movements lacked co-ordination and her hands appeared to be severely affected. With what was described as an 'apathetic and unresponsive appearance', her mental age was only a little above that of a normal child at 12 months. She suffered incontinence, a spastic condition of the legs and excessive salivation.

Over the next five years her condition improved slowly and marginally. In 1965 standard tests showed an IQ of 50. Muscular co-ordination was poor although by then she had learned to run a few steps and could remain on her feet. She could still understand only a few words of instruction but recognized the pictures and titling of children's programmes on television. Her pattern of brain activity was abnormal as recorded by electro-encephalogram, and she still had only clumsy use of her hands. It was then concluded that her condition would be one of permanent disablement.

Three cases out of 111, and perhaps already too morbid for some. Yet such details are essential to an understanding of the kind of poisons we are talking about, particularly at a time when human realities tend to become buried in statistics, and physical realities are often deliberately disguised by euphemisms. 'Minamata disease' is itself such a euphemism, for, although it was created out of ignorance to describe a peculiar set of symptoms, it has continued to be used in spite of the fact that the symptoms are not of a 'disease' but of acute mercurial poisoning from an industrial source.

THE INVESTIGATION

The Kumamoto investigation which led to that conclusion was painstaking, took two years of valuable time by a dozen or so physicians and scientists, and involved a whole series of animal experiments in attempts to reproduce the human symptoms. It is claimed by toxicologists in both Britain and Sweden that Minamata disease was recognized by them for what it was long before the Japanese investigators reached their conclusions. This may be the case but it receives no mention in the Japanese record, an indication that the international nature of medicine and science is by no means as closely interwoven as some would have us believe. National influences remain profound and, as will be seen later, serve as a barrier to the transmission of information so that the events in one country seldom alert others to the possibility of a repetition.

However, the Kumamoto investigators got down to their work with commendable speed. Giving first priority to a two-pronged attack aimed at plotting the distribution of the disease and identifying its cause, the scientists set about eliminating one by one the naturally occurring diseases and the compounds whose poisonous symptoms, although in some ways similar, did not fully tie in with those of the Minamata victims. By this time, September–October 1956, events along the coast were giving a decisive lead. Not only cats but other domestic animals began to go mad and die: the fish in Minamata Bay began to be washed up dying on the shores, and the wild birds which ate them, particularly carrion crows, began to stagger, convulse and die in large numbers. The 'disease' was spreading fast.

By November, having eliminated contagious encephalitis and other naturally occurring diseases, the study group turned to the possibility of heavy metal poisoning of some kind. The distribution of the disease (FIG. 1:1) revealed it to be concentrated primarily along the coast and, with the fish dying, it took no great leap of imagination to suggest a connection between the two. The diet of the peasant fishermen was, after all, based on the fish they caught, and studies showed that about 70% of the affected families either included fishermen among their members or at least one member who worked part-time as a fisherman. The field of search, although it went on properly to include the examination of drinking water and of the sewage system, began to narrow down. Armed with analytical techniques far less accurate and sophisticated than are available today, the Kumamoto study

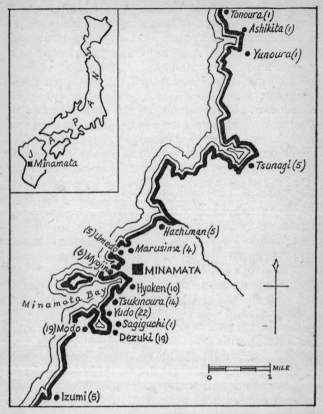

FIG. 1:1. Minamata and its surrounding villages: the figures in brackets show the number of cases of Minamata disease in each locality (derived from Kumamoto University report).

team began to examine fish and shellfish for toxic material.

Now certain that the *route* of the disease-causing poison had been found, the local authority banned all fishing in Minamata Bay. That meant, in effect, depriving the entire fishing community of both its livelihood and its main source of food. This, we must remember, was a stable rural community of 10,000 people living in a region which offered no alternative living and no immediate compensation. The investigation plodded on, coupled with careful studies of the symptoms of the victims, of the various forms taken by the disease, the effects of various treatments on its course and ultimately the evaluation of remedial techniques for those who survived. The future of anyone who developed advanced symptoms—and as will be explained later the Minamata studies take no account of the many people who were mildly affected but showed only one or two initial symptoms—was extremely gloomy. Only about 10% of those affected were able, eventually, to return to work. One third died, while the remainder suffered varying degrees of permanent disability.

BURDEN OF GUILT

That the culprit in this case was clearly a substance that devastated the central nervous system prompted the searchers to look in turn for thallium, lead, manganese and finally mercury. With mercury they hit the jackpot. Samples of mud from the bay close to the drainage point of factory effluent contained up to 2100 parts per million (ppm) wet weight of inorganic mercury. In shellfish in the bay the mercury content turned out to be between 27 and 100 ppm, although in this instance the figures relate to *dry* weight. On a similar basis, that in fish was between 5 and 15 ppm, giving an average of about 8 ppm. Confusion was to arise later because of the adoption by the Japanese of a dry weight basis, and minor diversion is needed to explain the trouble.

Fish, as they exist alive in the sea or on the wet fishmonger's slab, contain about 80% water. In general the concentrations of poisons found in them are expressed either as parts per million (or milligrams per kilogram) or as nanograms per gram, that is parts per billion, of the total wet weight of fish. If the concentration is expressed as a proportion of the residual weight after the water has been removed from the sample, then the figure will be 5 times higher. In other words 1·0 ppm wet weight equals 5·0 ppm dry weight. Curiously, the conversion factor often employed is 4 not 5, although the reason for this is obscure. It is, however, probably right in relation to canned fish.

However, translating the Japanese findings to the more familiar wet weight basis, the shellfish contained between 5·0 ppm and 20 ppm of organic mercury, and the fish between 1·0 ppm and 3·0 ppm. You would normally expect a deep sea fish to contain something like 0·05 to 0·1 ppm of total mercury, accumulated from the minute amounts naturally present in sea water. The investigators had undoubtedly found the source of the *human* poisoning, but they still had not identified the source for the *fish*. It seems likely that the levels of organic mercury in the dead and dying fish which at this time littered Minamata Bay were higher than in the living specimens. But when investigators of other countries came to calculate the daily intake of mercury by those who were affected at Minamata[2] it was assumed, probably rightly, that fishermen would never eat dead or obviously sick fish.

Yet, having led to a ban on fishing in the area and, provisionally at least, having identified the poison, the investigation had by no means reached its end. The unresolved problem was thorny. The mercury in the fish was organic, that is to say was contained in a chemical compound which also included carbon and hydrogen and was of the kind associated with living systems, and not of the kind associated with either the mud in the bay or with industrial processes. (Broadly speaking mercury can exist in three forms: the silvery metal which we know as quicksilver, inorganic compounds such as the mercuric chloride and mercuric sulphate used in industrial processes, and organic forms such as phenyl and dimethyl mercury. The organic forms are by far the most toxic and at this time, the mid-1950s, it was generally assumed that inorganic forms remained inorganic when discharged into rivers or into the sea. The assumption had not been tested and turned out to be one of the most appalling errors industrialists and effluent control authorities have ever made.)

So, blinkered by the lack of an essential piece of knowledge, the investigators looked with puzzlement on the discrepancy of their findings. To prove that they were dealing with organic mercury (and apparantly disregarding the existence of standard text books), experiments were undertaken with rats, cats and mice to show that relatively low doses of organic mercury of several kinds could produce symptoms that precisely mimicked those of Minamata disease. This took months and, in the meantime, the numbers of dead fish, dead crows and the extent of the affected area continued to grow.

The search for a source of organic mercury was stepped up. Agricultural and slaughter-house effluents which at several points entered directly into the bay came under suspicion, as did the numerous dumps of World War II ammunition that were known to be in and around the region of the bay. But, inevitably, the search finally came back to the industrial effluents of the large chemical factory at Minamata.

This had initially been a fertilizer plant but, after the war, it had been extended rapidly to embrace the production of plastics (PVC resins) and the large-scale production of the industrial chemicals octanol and dioctyl phthalate. In these processes acetaldehyde was used as an important intermediate, the acetaldehyde being synthesized in the plant by a process which used mercuric sulphate as a catalyst. Large-scale production of vinyl chloride began in 1952 shortly before the onset of the epidemic, reaching 1800 tons a year by 1960. The octanol plant expanded no less rapidly, increasing its annual output from 6000 tons in 1956 to 18,000 tons in 1960.

The untreated effluents from these processes were released into settling ponds and then allowed to flow via a canal into the bay. Where the effluent reached the estuary the water, not surprisingly, was found to be rich in several industrial metals, including lead, arsenic, zinc and manganese as well as mercury, a contingency which created new complexities. The situation was not eased by the curious fact that the plant's 'official' analysis of its effluents for the crucial year 1956 failed to include any mention of mercury.

However, with the permission of the factory management, which is acknowledged with touching grace by the Kumamoto University record, the mud of the settling pond was analysed and found to contain up to 700 ppm (wet weight) of inorganic mercury compounds, principally mercuric chloride and mercuric sulphide. No trace of organic mercury was found, a circumstance which set back the investigation and the application of effective control for 2 years and 4 years respectively.

But the ban on fishing proved to be effective for, although 6 congenitally affected infants came briefly into the world at Minamata in 1957, there were no new adult cases. Tentatively the investigators toyed with the possibility that in some way, as yet unknown, the inorganic mercury from the factory was being turned by natural processes into the deadly organic form. To the later cost of other countries the notion was never followed up, principally because, in early 1958, continuing investigations at the factory revealed the presence of a small proportion of organic mercury in some waste waters. It was also discovered that, although the continuous discharge of inorganic mercury in effluent was not on a scale large enough to have led to marine contamination of the extent reached in the bay, the acetaldehyde plant was cleaned out four times a year. In that process very large amounts of mercury were discharged.

Although in quantitative terms it did not make sense, the existence of organic mercury in the waste water and plant sludge was taken to clinch the case. Two steps were taken. First the chemical works began construction of an effluent treatment plant to eliminate the emission of heavy metals and, second, the discharge point for effluents was moved from the settling ponds and canal so that it discharged directly into the Minamata river. The idea,

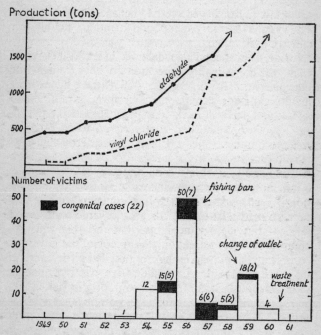

FIG. 1:2. Correlation between production at Minamata chemical factory and the number of cases of Minamata disease. Second outbreak, after change of outlet, is clearly shown.

presumably, was to achieve some dilution before it reached the sea but it led, in conjunction with a partial return to fishing by the peasant community, to a new outbreak of poisoning (FIG. 1:2).

There were 7 new cases in 1958, 2 of them foetal; 20 in 1959 with again, 2 foetal; and 4 adult cases in 1960. During these years it was found that the acetaldehyde plant was, in fact, grossly inefficient and was losing nearly a kilogram of mercury for every ton of acetaldehyde produced. That in itself must set a pathetic industrial record and it meant that about 200 *tons* of mercury had gone into the sea between 1949 and 1953, and that considerably more reached the bay between 1954 and 1960. The organic mercury compound identified in the acetaldehyde sludge and wash water was methyl mercuric chloride, a compound also identified in shellfish. Thus, by 1960, the investigation appeared to have things fully buttoned up and when, in early 1961, the effluent treatment plant came into use, the concentrations of mercury in fish and shellfish in the bay began to fall rapidly. By 1962 shellfish which had contained up to 25 ppm wet weight contained only 2·0 ppm. The tragedy had been played out.

In summing up the results of their investigation the Kumamoto study group made some false recommendations—such as stressing the importance of turning any organic mercurial effluent to an inorganic form before release—but also pointed out that in an increasingly complex effluent situation the regulations governing control and continual monitoring needed to be tightened up. This, they said, would not be the end of Minamata disease. Industrial control was so poor and the circumstances leading to contamination so diverse that new outbreaks of poisoning were almost certain to occur. As seems always to be the case no one took any notice.[3] The 'public nuisance' at Minamata had abated and apathy set in.

Within 4 years the Kumamoto prophecy had become reality—and not only in Japan. At Niigata City on the coast of the Sea of Japan about 170 miles north of Tokyo, in an area where the waters are both more open and more rapidly flushed by tidal action than at Minamata, effluent from a plastics factory led to a build up of organic mercury in fish and shellfish.[4] Again the symptoms went unrecognized for months and although when action came it was both earlier and more immediately effective than at Minamata, 28 people were severely affected and 5 of them died. This 'incident' confirmed some terrifying and highly significant things about methyl mercury poisoning. First, *the onset of symptoms is slow*, so that chronic exposure that would be disabling or lethal can take place for months without any sign of symptoms; second, that *when the symptoms begin to show up it is much too late to do anything to reverse the course of poisoning*, for the damage is already done and, because of the long residence time of organic mercury in the body—particularly in the brain—will continue and become permanent; third, that anyone who eats one normal meal of fish contaminated by organic mercury to levels of between 5·0 ppm and 15·0 ppm (wet weight) every day will most certainly be disabled and will probably die.

UNSEEN VICTIMS

The Japanese Ministry of Health reports on Niigata victims threw an even more sinister light on the real effects of the incident. In diagnosing mercury poisoning only those who showed a *complete complex of symptoms*, loss of feeling or co-ordination of limbs, numbness of mouth or face, and loss of vision, were officially classified as victims. There were, however, more than 120 other cases in which some of these symptoms appeared, but which were not included in the record. At Minamata, as already mentioned, only those with *advanced* symptoms were officially recorded as adult or child victims—with the exception of infants who suffered damage during pregnancy in apparently unaffected mothers.

The official figures, whether deliberately or not, therefore *minimize* the scale of poisoning. Taking the Niigata proportions as being roughly true for Minamata, we need to multiply the recorded cases by 5 to get at a reasonable figure for the number of people who reached that level of chronic poisoning at which first clinical symptoms appeared. That would give us 550 adults and children at Minamata (5·5% of the exposed population) and 140 at Niigata. But even these figures do not reveal the full extent of the damage. It is a normal practice in toxicology to assume that the 'no effect' dose of a poison is one-tenth of the minimum dose required to produce symptoms, and that the 'safe level' for whole-population exposures is again one-tenth of that. In other words, *below the tip of the pyramid of poisoning at which symptoms appeared there would be an area, ten times as large, in which varying degrees of damage would have been done, some undoubtedly of a permanent nature*. We are now talking about *more than half* of the exposed population, and since the Minamata and other incidents have demonstrated quite clearly that children and infants are probably *twice* as sensitive as adults to organic mercury poisoning, it seems likely that a very high proportion of the youngsters in the exposed populations will have been affected in some permanent and damaging way.

This, naturally enough, is not a view that is popular either with industry or with control agencies, governmental or otherwise. Quite apart from the natural if reprehensible desire of both industry and controlling agencies to conceal or minimize their blunders, there are some inbuilt and almost traditional reasons for failing to grasp the potential dangers of neurological poisoning by heavy metals. It is not that the dangers of mercury or, for that matter, lead were taken lightly by the toxicologists and other scientists who serve as advisors to Governments and to industries, but that their experience was and often still is of the wrong kind for the conditions that have accompanied the explosive expansion of technologies.

Experience with mercury, for instance, goes back to Classical times and in its underlying modern form was based on experience in industry and in medicine during the nineteenth century. It is confined almost exclusively to knowledge of the metal and of the various inorganic salts used in processes. In the seventeenth century surgeons

involved in the treatment of patients with mercurial oint-
ment for syphilis recognized the danger to themselves
through absorption of mercury through the skin, and
developing technological processes, such as the silvering
of mirrors, left a trail of casualties. Indeed it was the use
of mercuric nitrate in felt-making processes that led to the
traditional notions of 'hatter's shakes' and 'hatter's madness,' conditions that became common in the felt-handling
trades.

In virtually every trade where mercury was used problems arose and, over the years, led to preventive measures
and various kinds of industrial control. Before the end of
the nineteenth century 'mercurialism' became a notifiable
disease in Britain (although not elsewhere until much
later) and, at least within responsible industries, mercury
compounds were treated with considerable care and
respect. But all this experience, which showed that even
with long and severe exposure some recovery might be
expected, applied to *inorganic* substances. Organic
mercurials remained outside industrial experience until
the 1930s, although, before then, they had made a
startling entrance as new and highly potent poisons.[5]

In the course of research at St Bartholomew's Hospital,
London, di-methyl mercury was examined for its structure
in 1863. In 1866 the two laboratory technicians who had
been handling the material died after a long and increasingly severe neural disablement. In 1887 di-ethyl mercury
was introduced as treatment for syphilis in Germany.
Patients were given injections ranging from 0·1 to 1·0
millilitres of a 1% solution. The treatment was found to
be so toxic that no patient received more than two
injections, and the idea was abandoned. Yet, in spite of
their demonstrable and insidious toxicity, the examination
and industrial evaluation of organic mercurials continued.

Their fungicidal properties were noticed before World
War I and investigated in detail in the 1920s, leading to
the use of various organic mercurial compounds against a
large number of seed-borne diseases in the 1930s when

large-scale manufacture began. From that time onward the catalogue of poisoning incidents grew quickly. Animal experiments continued to confirm the fears that these compounds selectively destroyed areas of the central nervous system, and people handling them or working near to storage areas in industry continued to suffer death or disablement. There were four cases in England in 1940, and two deaths in Canada in 1943. A year later there were six deaths in Russia and, in 1946–7, five cases including two deaths in Sweden.

When this was reported by Dr A. Ahlmark[6] the world received its first scientific warning about the dangers of organic mercurials in the environment. One man had suffered disablement in spite of observing all the protective precautions in every detail, while another died after repeatedly using a methyl mercury hydroxide spray to protect wood. The doses in both cases appeared to be much lower than anyone at that time believed able to cause disablement, let alone death. Dr Ahlmark extrapolated from this the potential dangers both to human beings and to the environment, of the expanding use of these compounds in agriculture.

Characteristically, the warning fell on deaf ears. The practice was established and it continued to grow. In England in 1955 a nursery foreman died after using dilute solutions of ethyl mercury phosphate in greenhouses and, in two incidents in Iraq in 1956 and 1960, severe poisoning was suffered by about 350 people of whom 36 died. These were the first major incidents of mass poisoning through organic mercurial compounds and they occurred in a peasant population which ignored warnings about the making of bread from seed treated with fungicide. That they occurred at roughly the same time as the Minamata outbreak is simply a coincidence, although both reflect an irresponsible lack of understanding of the inherent dangers of mercury.

Accidental exposures and deaths continued but were, in a sense, disregarded by both Governments and controlling agencies. The situation is tersely summed up by Donald Hunter in his source book on occupational diseases. Before any understanding of the mystery of the Minamata outbreak was reached (and that did not occur until the mid-'sixties as the next chapter will show), he wrote:

Work published before 1940 made it clear that ethyl and methyl mercury compounds are so dangerous that they should never be manufactured again. The warning remains unheeded and the grim record of deaths occurring in many countries is a sad monument to the greed and stupidity of men. Since the phenyl and tolyl compounds of mercury are effective fungicides and since they are less dangerous and can be handled with safety, *only these* should be manufactured. ... The whole process of manufacture should be carried out mechanically for gloves and respirators are inadequate as a means of protection. ...

That warning, with its parallel warning that any attempt to prevent treated seed from being used as food in illiterate communities would 'usually' fail, continued to be ignored, as was the recommendation, made after the Iraq incidents, that seed treated with mercurial compounds should not only be dyed but treated with an additional compound that rendered the seed highly unpalatable and therefore unsuitable for use either in bread-making or as animal feeding stuff.

From all this it can be seen that, by the mid-'forties, there should have been a general awareness of the dangers of developments taking place in agriculture and in industry and that, had these dangers been heeded, the mass outbreaks of 1956 and later would never have happened. It was also obvious by then that the long industrial experience with inorganic mercurials had little relevance to the newer organic materials for these were not only more potent but more terrible in their effects.

Although in some ways the symptoms of chronic exposure to inorganic mercury are similar to those of exposure to the organic forms—loss of co-ordination, vision and hearing certainly occur—there is one very large difference between the two forms. Organic mercury, simply because of its chemistry, becomes firmly bound to various proteins and fats which make up the cells that structure the body. Inorganic compounds do not. This means that the residence time in the body of organic mercurials is very much greater than that of their inorganic brothers. To describe this residence time scientists now use a very convenient measure called the 'half-life' of a substance, a term originally developed by physicists to describe the rate at which a radioactive substance decayed. Used in its biological sense (at least in this context) it means the length of time needed for a system to get rid of half the poison it has absorbed.

In the case of *inorganic* mercury the half-life in humans and most mammals is about 6 days. This means that it is swept up fairly rapidly by the body's natural detoxification systems. In turn that means that the mercury concentrates rapidly in the liver and kidneys where, if the dose is large enough, massive damage can occur. But, in the case of *organic* mercurials the half-life is about 70 days [7] a characteristic which completely changes the chronic level of exposure that can lead to severe poisoning (FIG. 1:3). It can be seen that, with a daily intake of 2 milligrams a day of *inorganic* mercury, the total body burden will not reach 20 milligrams however long the exposure. In the case of *organic* mercury the body-burden would top 200 milligrams within a year, although death would intervene long before then!

Anomalous accumulation is especially true of mercury in its organic forms because, although the whole body half-life averages out at around 70 days, different organs handle the invasive material differently and therefore have differing individual half-lives. While it is well known that various radioactive isotopes are, as it were, target-selective (and therefore end up in different concentrations in different organs), it is less well recognized that, in the case of organic poisons, even the best biologically protected areas, such as the brain or the foetus, are endangered by a disproportionately long half-life in spite of their slow rate of take-up of the poison.

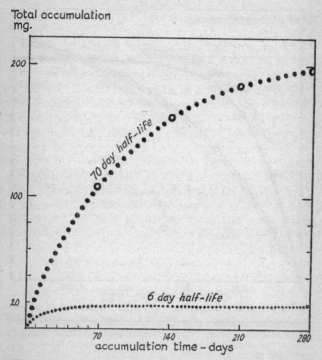

FIG. 1:3. The effect of different periods of half-life on accumulation in the body. Organic mercury reaches 10 times the level of inorganic mercury in 9 months. (At the 2 milligram per day ingestion level shown here symptoms of severe poisoning from organic mercury would in fact appear before the third month.)

This is probably best illustrated by yet another diagram (FIG. 1:4) in which it is assumed that, of a daily intake of 100 micrograms of organic mercury, 50 micrograms are absorbed into the liver while only 20 micrograms are absorbed into the brain. But the brain has a half-life that is much longer than that of the liver. (The half-lives shown in the chart, 150 days and 50 days, are arbitrary but may well be close to the truth.) The result is that within a

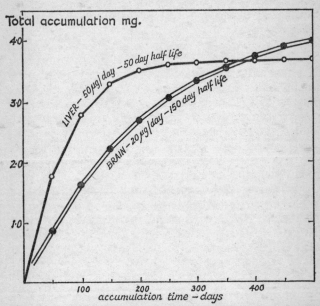

FIG. 1:4. Accumulation in brain and liver assuming 20% and 50% absorption respectively of a daily dose of 100 micrograms—and a longer brain half-life. A dose of 100 micrograms would be contained in a normal single meal of fish that contained 0·5 ppm mercury (the permitted maximum in the US and Canada). Brain half-life is not known accurately but is believed to be considerably longer than that of the liver. Half-life in the testes is also long. According to some scientists, symptoms of damage to the brain first appear at concentrations as low as 3 micrograms per gram of brain tissue—which would be reached in 50 days on this half-life basis. Other scientists believe that 20 micrograms per gram of brain tissue is the damage symptom threshold.

few months the concentrations of poison in the organs are not very different and, within a year, the *brain* concentration is higher *even though its daily uptake is less than half that of the liver*. What is more—and this explains the devastating effects of organic mercury poisoning—the cells of the *nervous system* and particularly those of parts of the *brain* appear to be more easily damaged by mercury than are the cells of other organs. In Minamata victims it was found that complete layers of the cerebellum had been destroyed.

Now brain cells are very special and not only because through their development and use they determine our ability to think, co-ordinate and perform in a more sophisticated and complex way than any other kind of animal. They are special because *we are endowed with a limited number of brain cells at birth*. They do not reproduce themselves and their repair mechanisms are less complete than those of some other cells. This means that, from the time of birth, the number of brain cells decays steadily through natural processes.

At the outset the convoluted sheath of grey matter that is called the cerebral cortex contains something like 10 thousand million interconnected neural cells, with perhaps a further 2 thousand million in the connected but structurally differentiated area, the cerebellum. Quite apart from being a still mysterious and most extraordinary piece of biological structure in which nature has managed to pack and interconnect in a volume of about 300 cubic centimetres (18 cubic inches) a mass of cells which in number roughly equal four times the total human population of the earth, the cells themselves and their interconnection both differ from those which carry messages around the body.

These messages or signals, which travel along nerve pathways called axons, are electrochemical. One of the minor miracles of this communications system is that although different axons may be separated by very short distances, perhaps one thousandth of a millimetre (and then of material mainly composed of conducting salts) there is virtually no cross-interference between messages. This is to do with the electrical shape of the signal which moves along the axon like an extended but totally enclosed smoke ring producing hardly any electrical disturbance outside itself. But the important difference between the axons outside the brain and the neural connections within it is in the structure of the conducting fibre.

Axons of the neural pathways in our limbs, for example, are encased in a very thin sheath which appears to endow them with the property of regeneration. If, through damage of some kind, an axon is severed, then the severed part will wither, break down chemically and be carried away by the body's natural clearing-up mechanisms through the bloodstream. But the part of the axon still attached to its neural cell will grow again along the original path so that the damaged network eventually becomes fully operational again. Not so in the brain. There the neural fibres interconnecting the billions of cells possess no outer sheath. Once a connection is damaged or broken then it remains useless for the rest of life.

NO SECOND CHANCE

So there are two immensely important factors which make damage to the brain extremely serious. First the neural cells of which it is composed cannot replicate and therefore, once seriously damaged or killed, cannot be replaced. Second the interconnections are not self-repairing, and again, once damaged, go out of action for ever. In the normal course of ageing, cells and their inter-connections slowly degenerate and their loss reveals itself in the declining powers and ultimate incapacity of brain function in old age. There is nothing, at least at the moment, that can be done about this natural decay: but it is quite obvious that any additional damage *should be avoided at all costs*.

Yet another important point has to be borne in mind when weighing the effects of any poisonous substance capable of damaging the nervous system or the brain. Functions such as seeing or the co-ordination of movements or, indeed, any activity, are not the outcome of the activity of single neural cells. All are the outcome of processes which involve thousands and probably millions of interconnected cells. Such systems have what electronic engineers are prone to call a high level of redundancy. That means that many pathways are not strictly necessary for the function to be carried out efficiently, but simply duplicate or triplicate other pathways in case some kind of blockage or breakdown occurs.

This needs weighing very carefully when considering the effects of organic mercury, or lead, or the many organochlorine and other pesticides which, like DDT, can incapacitate neural systems. For it means that by the time clinical symptoms of nervous disorder appear, such as lack of co-ordination or loss of vision, then enormous damage has already been done to the structure of the brain. It also means that quite extensive damage can be done without any clinical symptoms ever becoming detectable. This, in relation to heavy metals, is a terrifying situation.

It also explains why it is improper, if not wholly irresponsible, to measure the damage to humanity of incidents like those at Minamata or Niigata solely in terms of people who suffered obvious and extensive disruption of neural and brain function. For, as already suggested, below this tip of obvious and recognizable immediate suffering there must be a very much larger number of people who have suffered permanent brain damage whose extent ranges across a whole spectrum from mild to extremely serious without offering the slightest clinical symptom that can, at the present time, be 'officially' recognized.

The higher sensitivity of infants and children, although not understood, adds to the seriousness. Sensitivity could be the result of the brain possessing, in these early stages, fewer redundant pathways in the developing functional systems. This would mean an earlier breakdown of function in the event of widespread damage. But, from the permanence of residual damage it seems that brain cells not at that time involved in developed functional systems become incapacitated and never develop to play their full roles. It is hardly possible to conceive of a more dangerous and more damaging situation than that of an invisible and insidious contaminant that can produce such hidden effects. But that is the nature of organic mercury.

It happens that, even today, such 'sub-clinical' effects are not widely recognized either by medical authorities or by Government or industrial advisory bodies, a point which will be discussed later. But, back in the 'sixties when the full implications of the disasters at Minamata and Niigata were dawning on biologists (and, in particular, on radiobiologists who had experience of organ-selectivity of compounds and of the effects of difference of half-life), authorities in general were totally unresponsive to the danger that had been revealed. They appeared to be blinded by the arrogant but widespread belief that the various national systems of protection against this kind of contamination were so much better than that of Japan, notoriously casual at that time in her quest for exploitation and technological growth, that they would be immune to mercury problems.

Perhaps, in the early 'sixties when Minamata was becoming a bad memory which everyone wanted to forget as soon as possible, the view was dominated by the kind of expediency which, without any consultation of the public, led to the establishment of nuclear safety standards for whole populations which could ultimately permit a doubling of the natural background radiation dose. The argument behind this appears to be partly that if there is some there already which does not appear to do any harm, then twice as much will do no harm either. Biologically, the justification of the argument rests on the ability of living cells to repair a limited amount of damage as part of their natural function, but no one really knows what the effects of a doubling of radiation exposure will be. Indeed the right of Governments or industries to make such decisions—and on this one rests the whole future of nuclear power—is only just being seriously challenged by the public and by some radiobiologists who believe that the hazards have been inadequately assessed and that the dangers of nuclear proliferation have been inadequately explained.

The real situation is that a great deal remains unknown. Increased levels of radiation due to civil nuclear installations (barring incidents such as those at Windscale in England and in fuel processing plants in the US) are so far extremely small. The long-term experiment that will finally clinch the argument has yet to be made on us. This is not something that science can decide. *Research can only reduce the areas of uncertainty*. The decision must finally rest on a balancing of the advantages to be gained by the pursuit of a particular technological line against the hazards it involves.[8]

It happens that in the case of *radiation* hazards, which were seen to be extremely serious from the 1930s onward, an enormous expenditure of money and manpower was put into reducing uncertainties, particularly in the decade after World War II. There are still many areas of doubt and some of controversy, but the general level of information about public hazards is probably higher in this field than in any other. No such comparable research backs our knowledge of heavy metals.

Yet, in the nuclear field, even with the enormous research effort that went into the assessment of hazards, Governments committed to programmes of weapons testing were only with great difficulty and long delays persuaded that there were serious public hazards associated with fallout, particularly the fallout of strontium-90. Strontium, a white metal, is fairly rare on earth where it exists mainly as a naturally occurring sulphate. The radioactive isotope strontium-90 is man-made through nuclear explosions and, since strontium is mistaken for calcium by body mechanisms, it tends to accumulate in bone where its radioactivity can hammer bone-marrow cells. Hence it carries a high risk of bone tumours and of leukaemia, a risk which eventually led to the partial test-ban treaty that France and China continue to ignore. It seems unlikely that anyone will ever be able accurately to assess the global effects of fallout, but it is quite certain that without the dedicated efforts of a handful of physicists and radiobiologists of conscience, working mainly behind a high security wall, the commitment of defence agencies and Governments coupled with public ignorance imposed by security would have continued irresponsibly to lead the world towards greater biological disaster.

Because it is already well documented[9] and presents a special case, the strontium-90 story is really outside the scope of the study of heavy metals, but the pattern of events and the wilfully blind single-mindedness of the technological developments which led to danger are fairly typical of parallel events in the Government-industrial-civil field. First, there is the failure to carry out essential research in order to narrow the areas of uncertainty of effect. Second, there is the failure in communication, either because of 'security' (a most convenient blanket term) or because of ignorance. Ultimately, there is the basic inability (because of commitment) to grasp the true hazards of a situation—for recognition means not only the abandonment of an entrenched policy but also the admission, albeit tacit, of errors.

PATTERNS OF DISASTER

Looking back at the Minamata affair all these aspects of the pattern can be seen as elements in the eventual local disaster. Because of the pressure for rapid technological expansion in the post-war years the control of industrial effluent was lax. Even though it seems most unlikely that any industrial chemist or chemical engineer of the late 'forties and early 'fifties would be unaware of the dangers even of inorganic mercury, no attempt was made to limit the discharge into the sea. A total failure of communication seems to have led to a situation in which the local medical and health authorities were quite unaware of the large amounts of mercury reaching their environment, an ignorance which in turn led to great delay in locating the cause of public disaster. While it is perfectly true that the kind of brain encephalitis resulting from mercury poisoning (or for that matter from lead poisoning) is all too easy to confuse with the similar clinical symptoms produced by tumours or by several brain diseases caused by microbes of one kind or another, knowledge of a large local discharge of mercury would have led the local health authorities to a rapid and accurate diagnosis of the trouble *even though at that time no one understood the mechanisms which in nature transform inorganic mercury into the more deadly organic form.*

Whether the omission of mercury from the official analysis of the Minamata factory effluent indicates an innocent, if disastrous, oversight or something more sinister will never be known, but it seems a most extraordinary failure in the light of both the known toxicity of mercury and the very high rate at which the mercury catalyst was at that time being consumed by the acetaldehyde plant. However, the unfortunate truth is that those involved and probably culpable at Minamata and, later, elsewhere in Japan, were by no means alone in their failure to foresee the effects of mercury in the environment, or in their inability to grasp the implications of the widespread damage along the coast of Kyushu. In 1960 mercury problems were already threatening several parts of the world but, apart from a few lonely scientific voices —mainly in Sweden—the attitude was one of disinterest and apathy.

As will be seen, the world is still paying a high price for that disinterest, and the delays in recognizing the growing extent of mercurial contamination were the result of a curious inability of the various parts of Government, regulatory and industrial structures to recognize (or accept) warning signs so that a response could precede widespread damage. It is *not* inherently impossible to have continual changes of industrial or agricultural practice without environmental disasters, but the goal of profit blunts vision and the protective machinery of government, whether national or local, is locked in the lethargy produced in the process of acceptance by default. Almost by definition 'technological growth and development' is regarded by Governments as a Good Thing. That in itself may be utterly wrong but the truth is that, *at the present time, it seems always to require disaster before Governments will move.*

POSTSCRIPT

Widespread anger developed in Kyushu during the Minamata affair and, when it became known that the Minamata chemical plant was involved in the release of mercury, those deprived of a living by the fishing ban and those whose families had suffered casualties several times attacked the factory. Neither the local nor central Governments would pay the compensation that was demanded, and at no time have the factory authorities admitted that they were in any way responsible. In November 1959 about 3000 fishermen and other peasant workers stormed the factory, but were eventually beaten off by police. Those identified as leaders of the attack were brought to trial, and punished. Finally local politicians intervened and, after negotiations (by its own experiments the company then knew its effluents were to blame), the company agreed to pay token damages. Relatives of adult victims received the equivalent of £100 ($250) and those of infant victims, £30 ($75). In exchange the company denied liability in any way and further, demanded that those receiving compensation should sign a document which not only precluded the possibility of legal action on the basis of events up to that time, but precluded all action for further compensation even if 'at some future time the Minamata disease is proven to be the result of waste water from the plant.'[10] Nine years later, after the outbreak of poisoning at Niigata, the Japanese Ministry of Health finally stepped in with new regulations governing the discharge of mercurial wastes. There is evidence, however, that even by 1971 these had not been effectively applied.

Notes and References

1. Minamata Disease: Kumamoto University, Japan, 1968. A summary of papers published by the Minamata Study Group from 1958 onward, and covering epidemiology: clinical investigations (5 papers including rehabilitation): pathology: animal experiments with organomercury compounds and analytical determination of organic mercurials: toxicology in rats, investigation of the course of Minamata disease and Minamata disease 'as a public nuisance.'

2. L. T. Kurland and others: *World Neurology* 1 (1960), p 370.

3. Although not published in the collected form until 1968, individual papers by the Minamata Disease Study Group reached the scientific literature from 1958 onward. The Group's comments and warnings were probably known to the authorities well before 1960.

4. Reports on the mass mercury poisoning in the lower Agano River, Ministry of Health, Tokyo, Japan, 1966 and 1968.

5. See *The Diseases of Occupations* by Donald Hunter (English Universities Press, revised 1969) which gives well documented and highly readable histories of industrial poisoning problems.

6. A. Ahlmark: *British Journal of Industrial Medicine*, vol 5:117, 1948.

7. L. Eckman and others: *Nordic Medicine*, vol 79:450 and 456, 1968.

8. This point is discussed at greater length in *Science and Survival* by Professor Barry Commoner (first published in the

US in 1963 but republished in the UK by Ballantine/Pan in 1971).

9. *Nuclear Disaster* by Tom Stonier (Penguin Special: 226, 1965) is among the best popular analyses of the effects of nuclear fallout. A dramatic interpretation of the possible dangers of the expanding nuclear power programme is contained in *The Perils of the Peaceful Atom* by R. Curtis and E. Hogan (Gollancz: 1970) although this account has been sharply criticized on technical grounds.

10. *Medical News Tribune*, May 22 1970.

CHAPTER TWO

DISEASE AND BLINDNESS SPREAD

With events like Minamata in the record it is hardly surprising that popular environmental protection movements direct their fiercest criticism at industry. Thus the pro-survival philosophy underlying notions of environment protections has been identified as anti-technological. In an ideal world this need not be the case but the events of the late 'fifties and early 'sixties outside Japan did more to justify than to belie the notion. That the disaster in Japan had no impact whatever on the official protection agencies of the West is clear from Government and other publications at the time which hardly mention heavy metals as a hazard. Meanwhile a mercury problem of enormous significance was creeping up on the world.

From 1940 onward organic mercury compounds were increasingly introduced into agriculture as protective seed dressings, while the use of related compounds expanded in the paper industry, where they serve as pulp slimicides. The largest expansion of agricultural use occurred in Japan, North America and in the Scandinavian countries, Denmark, Sweden and Finland. It was believed, and given official support, that alkyl mercury seed dressings increased the yield of grain crops and, having endorsed that view, Government departments of agriculture pursued it with all the economic and technical arguments they could muster. What happened in Sweden is now regarded as a classic example of the blindness that can result from departmental fragmentation and from policy commitment. Those looking at crop yields were aware only of numbers; those looking at animal health saw only farm and domestic disease, and those looking at pollution measured smoke and dust and SO_2. Meanwhile nature died.

As is so often the case the first voices to be raised in protest in a developing environmental crisis came from outside the official encampments. From the early 'fifties onward Swedish naturalists began to report unusually high death rates among wild seed-eating birds such as the pigeon, partridge and pheasant. The suggestion of a relationship between the large numbers of deaths and the widespread introduction of methyl mercury seed dressings was dismissed by the authorities who refused to investigate. Yet, by the mid-'fifties, biochemists outside Government (and some inside) were already convinced that the connection was not only possible but probable and, to Sweden's good fortune, began an independent investigation based initially on the department of radiobiology in the biochemistry department of the University of Stockholm.

By the end of the 'fifties the environmental situation was worse. Naturalists were now reporting the disappearance of several species of birds of prey. The white-tailed eagle, the eagle owl, the peregrine, kestrel and harrier all decreased in number and some vanished entirely from former breeding grounds. Where species survived, breeding success was severely reduced and, in many locations, eggs were increasingly infertile. Naturalist and conservation societies, aware that pesticides might be to blame yet also convinced of a connection with methyl mercury, put pressure on the Swedish Ministry of Agriculture. Analyses had revealed high mercury levels in those dead birds of prey which had been examined and, in 1962, the Ministry's central seed testing institute recommended a 'voluntary reduction' of mercury compounds in commercial seed dressing.

Such a measure, almost certain to be ineffective, was more a sop to allay rising pressure than a genuine attempt to meet the situation. But by then the investigations initiated at Stockholm University, which had gained the support of biochemists elsewhere in the country, including some in Government laboratories, were beginning to bear rich and alarming fruit.

Through the development of neutron activation analysis the Swedish scientists had a highly sensitive technique for determining low levels of mercury (although at this stage the detection of methyl or other organic mercury still presented very great analytical difficulty). In 1963, the first reports of generally elevated mercury levels began to appear. Swedish eggs and meat were found to contain more mercury than those of neighbouring countries and, in 1964, it was discovered that the mercury levels of freshwater fish were in some localities disturbingly high. Sweden makes considerable commercial use of her freshwater fisheries and, with the example of Minamata very much alive in the minds of scientists if not of the Government, it was suddenly clear to them that a potentially disastrous mercury problem was already at hand. Individually, Government authorities in Sweden failed to act but, through a confrontation in parliament, a Commission was appointed to gather information. Its findings were presented in 1965 when, in paper after paper, the major outlines of the overall picture of severe and widespread mercury contamination were drawn with indisputable clarity. This was almost exactly 10 years after Göran Löfroth and others at Stockholm University had seen the danger.

COMPLACENCY UNMASKED

At this time, with Japan suffering a new outbreak of mercury poisoning at Niigata, Professor G. Westöö announced the preliminary finding—based on a refined gas chromatographic technique—that the mercury in Swedish fish was in the dimethyl form, already confirmed as the most deadly. Official inaction ended abruptly with a Royal Ordinance on October 15 1965, which among other things made compulsory the formerly voluntary reductions in alkyl mercury seed dressing, instituted a thorough-going and fully-backed investigation of the situation and eventually up-rooted and reorganized the whole environmental protection system. For Sweden, a fish-eating nation, the widespread contamination of inland lakes was immensely serious. With the spectre of a national epidemic of crippling brain damage in the background, a thorough-going investigation of mercury levels in the fish of inland waters was given high priority.

Pike, which sit at the top of the aquatic food chain, were used as an indicator species and were found, in various rivers and lakes, to have mercury concentrations ranging up to 17 ppm in their flesh.[1] In many streams, however, the concentrations of mercury in edible fish were found to be low, often less than 0·2 ppm. The pattern that emerged, of a correlation between *industrial* contamination and high mercury concentrations, rather than of contamination from run-off from *agricultural* land, was unexpected. As in Japan it failed to make sense, for although the mercury in fish was found to be almost entirely in the dimethyl form, industrial losses were predominantly inorganic. The exception was slimicide but this, although organic, was not dimethyl.

When it came, the explanation was explosive. It had already been suggested that in mammals and fish inorganic mercury can be converted into an organic form in the liver. (Microbiologists since then have also suggested that this can happen in the gut.) But in 1967 workers at the Swedish Air and Water Pollution Research Laboratory, which had been at the centre of the freshwater investigation, came up with a finding which unmasked a frightening situation.[2] Inorganic mercury could be transformed *naturally* in the aquatic environment into the deadly dimethyl form. It was suggested that this occurred through microbial action in anaerobic (oxygen depleted) conditions, such as those in the sediments of lakes and rivers. A year later the finding was confirmed. *Any* mercury entering the environment could be methylated so as to enter food chains in its most insidious form. The Japanese mystery was solved,[3] as was the apparent inconsistency of finding only dimethyl mercury in fish.

But the problem, for Sweden and for the rest of the world, became one not only of control of alkyl mercurials in agriculture (whose reduction, incidentally, did not reduce crop yields in Sweden), but one concerning mercury in whatever form it was used. The major problems and major potential sources were most probably industrial.

Up to this time the industrial nations of the world had based their assumptions about the toxicity of inorganic mercurial effluents largely on the accumulated evidence of the industrial exposure of workpeople. Compared to the organic forms toxicity was low, with the result that large amounts of inorganic mercurials had been allowed to flow into rivers and estuaries in the belief that through dispersal and binding on to sediments these would do little harm. The appalling error of this assumption had been revealed by a single discovery which, with proper diligence, might have been made at least ten years earlier.

Many of the implications it carried were unravelled in Sweden in the second half of the 'sixties when the continued monitoring of wildlife, the investigation of lake life (and of sediments), the examination of foodstuffs and exposed populations and the calculation of the build-up of mercurials in the food chain, all revealed a complex situation that in one aspect was much worse than might have been predicted by the most extreme pessimist. The abrupt reduction in the use of alkyl mercury seed dressings and in the use of phenyl mercury acetate as a pulp industry slimicide did not lead to parallel improvements. While some recovery in bird-life was apparent within two years, there was no improvement *at all* in the levels of contamination of freshwater and estuarial fish.

Early in 1966 the Swedish authorities held an information conference that indicated quite conclusively that most industrial nations could expect to find a mercury problem if they looked. Denmark, Norway and Finland who took an official and serious look, found this to be true. Finland in particular, with her extensive paper pulp industry, discovered not only generally elevated levels of mercury in foodstuffs but widespread contamination of inland waters. Britain, the US, Canada and other countries represented at the conference, hardly looked at all.

HOT NUMBERS

Yet it was known by this time, from the Minamata and Niigata poisonings, that quite incredibly small amounts of organic mercury in the daily diet could lead to crippling results. Fired by the discovery of natural methylization and the Swedish discovery of patchwork contamination containing localized and long-lived 'hot-spots' where fish were potentially dangerous, an international assault on the problem might have been expected. It did not materialize. Mercury remained, in most countries, under 'voluntary' control in industry. Meanwhile, looking at the related problem of mercurials in pesticides, a joint working party of the UN Food and Agriculture Organization and the World Health Organization had come up with a very significant recommendation. It was impossible, they said, to demonstrate a 'no-effect' level for organic mercurials in animal studies:

> 0·1 ppm, equivalent to 0·005 milligrams per kilogram of body weight per day, produces a slight effect in the rat. Even if this figure were to be adopted as a maximum no-effect level and the customary safe factor applied, this would give an acceptable daily intake for man of 0·00005 milligrams per kilogram body-weight. This is tantamount to zero. It is undesirable that for the general population there should be any increase in the natural intake of mercury.[4]
>
> (*The recommendation amounts to maximum permissible daily dose of 3 micrograms for the average person, very much less than the average daily intake of about 30 micrograms of naturally occurring mercury in food.*)

In Sweden scientists involved in the mercury investigation concluded that it would be advisable, in the case of fish for human consumption, to establish a maximum permissible level of 0·5 ppm (wet weight). Initially, this was recommended by the Swedish Institute of Public Health (November 1966), but when a formal recommendation was made in February 1967 the ceiling had been raised to 1·0 ppm. The change has not been fully explained although the original calculation used for the setting of the Swedish standard was shown to be erroneous and another has been substituted to give the same result.

In the first 'official' toxicological evaluation the argument ran like this:

In Minamata about 88* persons in 10,000 were affected. They ate, generally every day, fish and shellfish with a mercury content of 27–102 ppm, an average of 50 ppm. According to toxicological experience a decrease of mercury content of the fish to one tenth of the Minamata values (i.e. about 5 ppm) should prevent the appearance of poisonings. With a further decrease of the mercury content to 0·5–1·0 ppm, one can reasonably exclude the influence of methyl mercury even with the daily consumption of fish. According to this evaluation fish with a mercury content above 1·0 ppm must be regarded as unfit for human consumption. . . . The safety factor is, however, low, perhaps no higher than 5.[5]

(*For simplicity mercury concentrations have been translated from mg/kg to ppm.*)

That sounds reassuring, but almost immediately the evaluation came under fierce criticism because it contained a serious error. The Minamata concentrations had been calculated in relation to dry weight, whereas they had been interpreted by the Swedish authorities as wet weight. The difference is considerable. Since fish contain 80% water, a dry weight concentration of 50 ppm is equivalent to a wet weight concentration of only 10 ppm.

* This was the total at that time.

This meant that the ceiling should have been stated as between 0·2 and 0·5 ppm not 1·0 ppm. In December 1967 the Swedish recommendation was changed. The permitted maximum limit of 1·0 ppm was retained (on the basis of a different calculation) but the public was advised not to eat fish from fresh or coastal water more than once a week. This extraordinary and impossible recommendation still stands.

Prof Göran Löfroth, in the methyl mercury survey from which these points are taken, only hints at an explanation of the anomaly. But the banning of fish sales from commercial inland lakes was bound to result from the setting of a standard. By the end of 1966 it was known that fish in Lake Vänern, Sweden's biggest commercial lake, had concentrations above 0·5 ppm. Public health, it seems, did not have absolute priority.

When a fishing ban was applied only 1·0% of inland waters were in fact affected although, had the maximum permitted level of 0·5 ppm been applied—as was later adopted by both Canada and US—rather more than 45% of Sweden's inland fisheries would have been put out of action.

However, the stimulation given to scientific research on the effects of mercury was soon to lead to new and, in some ways, even more disturbing findings than that of extreme direct toxicity to man. An investigation of the movement of the mercury residues from spraying on fruit trees had, back in 1959, indicated that 'translocation' occurred. There was a rapid penetration of bark and tissue and the mercury tended to concentrate in the fruit.[6] This had been confirmed by later research in Canada. But, during the period 1967–70 it was shown that mercury from seed dressings could pass into cereal grain and that, in rice, the mercury of seed coatings passed up into the growing plant. In general it seems that, while inorganic mercurials are not taken up by the plant, organic mercurials tend to be absorbed and concentrated in specific regions much as they are concentrated in particular organs in mammals. But absorption is *not through the roots.*

This means that the *fallout* of mercury onto crops may be biologically as significant as the presence of mercury in water or soil and that a complete understanding of likely concentration routes through plants and animals requires a very large-scale investigation. One certain implication is that unpredictable concentrations will occur, a point given sinister significance by other findings made by Swedish and American scientists during the same period. Organic mercury, it was discovered, is highly mutagenic and at low concentrations in humans can lead to chromosome breaks. In plants it disrupts the chromosome distribution during cell division, resulting in a high incidence of abnormalities.[7] When added to its known properties of concentrating in the testes as well as the brain, of crossing the placental barrier to disrupt the developing central nervous system of the foetus, and of methylating naturally, the gross folly of the indiscriminate disposal of mercurial wastes becomes all too clear.

Since world mercury production had risen rapidly up to 1960 and since mercury was being increasingly used in chemical processes (FIG. 2:1) there was by 1967 enough solid evidence to suggest that a global pollution problem might exist. Although the genetic findings were not published until December, a joint meeting of the UN World Health Organization and the Food and Agricultural Organization sponsored by the International Atomic Energy Agency in Amsterdam in May had already issued a warning. In a recommendation which expunged all previous WHO mercury standards for foods it was announced that new and detailed studies of mercury levels in human tissues were urgently needed. Without these it was 'not possible to set meaningful maximum permissible limits for dietary intakes.' The meeting recommended that every effort should be made to control and 'reduce this form of contamination' of the environment, and member Governments were advised as a matter of urgency to establish national monitoring systems.

This sense of urgency seems, almost universally, to have failed to reach executive levels in Government. Complacency appears to have been dominant in official circles in both Britain (where mercury had been subject to industrial control for about 70 years and where the

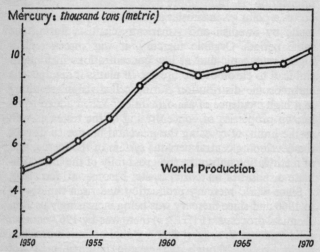

FIG. 2:1. World production of mercury. After a period of stability during the 'sixties production is again rising and will be three times the 1950 figure by 1975. Major new use is in chlor-alkali plants.

Government Chemist was already setting up a small generalized food sampling system), and in the United States, where neither good industrial control nor national mercury food-monitoring existed. Oddly, on one aspect at least, things were probably better in the US than elsewhere in the world because a Federal Drug Administration ruling of 1964 which strictly limited the amount of mercury that could be permitted in food wrapping paper (which Canada also followed) had resulted in a sharp decline in the use of mercurial slimicides. One of the spurs to complacency—if the contradiction can be permitted—was that wherever measurements had been made, such as in shellfish off the US coast and in British waters, mercury levels were low. Since shellfish are generally good pollution indicators (because of their rapid concentration of metals to several hundred times the level of the water in which they live), this finding was taken to be reassuring. The need to *look* for mercury 'hot spots', demonstrated in Sweden, was not grasped.[21]

The extreme persistence of mercury contamination in rivers and lakes, through binding on to sediments and slow methylation, was amply demonstrated in Sweden and Finland, as was the characteristic development of 'hot spots' in inland waters. National monitoring techniques were designed around the need to keep an eye on such things as radioactive fallout and pesticides, both of which tend toward a uniform distribution. Mercury, however, tends to disperse slowly, simply because it is firmly bound to sediments and, if methylated, is rapidly taken up by local organisms. This means that it is possible for a river to have stretches of a few miles around mercurial effluent point in which the general level of contamination of fish is much higher than indicated by water or fish samples farther down stream. The problems are obviously of highest potential intensity in lakes with a fairly slow water turnover, and perhaps in slow tidal reaches of rivers where contaminated water may move up and down several times over the same area. But the point is that uneven distribution is the rule, so any meaningful survey needs to seek out those areas of contamination likely to add significant quantities of mercury to the local diet. There is little to be gained, except false reassurance, from the kind of 'shopping basket' survey normally carried out in Britain, the United States, Russia and most European countries.

DEADLY TENTACLES

Since the razor's edge between continued health and possible disability is only a few hundred millionths of a gram in width, a daily diet which for a few weeks happens to include even mildly contaminated shellfish can sway the issue. During 1967–8, in spite of the UN WHO recommendation neither the US nor Britain took the warning seriously. Things were taking a different course in Canada. Scientists at the University of Toronto and at the University of Western Ontario, triggered by the events and findings in Sweden and Japan, concluded that the Canadian lakeland areas deserved investigation. Dr Robert Jervis at Toronto was already equipped to carry out the necessary refined analyses and, at Western Ontario, postgraduate students under Prof. W. Holsworth applied for and received a Government grant for a mercury survey. (Norvald Fimreite led this team.)

The findings were startling. Fish in Lake St Clair and the St Clair river on the Canadian–US border were found to contain mercury in concentrations up to 7·8 ppm, well above the humanly fatal levels deduced from the Niigata disaster. The Canadian Government, whose fisheries and game authorities had been following the Scandinavian developments closely, promptly banned local fishing and extended the survey, for there are many relatively isolated communities in Canada whose food sources include local fisheries. Fears were confirmed in November 1969 when the Saskatchewan authorities reported extensive contamination in their river system. Although Canada is not widely industrialized it soon became clear that the mercury problem was widespread.

Even these neighbourly discoveries did not immediately stimulate official and urgent attention in the US. But in December 1969, when the accidental use of mercury dressed seed as food for the family pigs led to the neural devastation of the Huckleby family in New Mexico, there was a dramatic explosion of public and US Government concern. That the special and environmentally irrelevant case of tragedies involving the four Huckleby children, all irreparably damaged by mercury poisoning, should lead to a massive investigation of the environment is perhaps typical of the way issues become resolved through confusion. The Huckleby food chain—grain, pig, man—is no indicator of the immensely complex food chains of aquatic systems. But the Huckleby tragedy, highlighted by the appalling nature of the children's injuries, formed the nucleus around which the whole mercury problem condensed both in the corridors of US officialdom and in the public media.[8]

Briefly a kind of confused panic pervaded the scene. The US Department of Agriculture slapped a ban on mercury seed dressings only to be taken to court by the manufacturers. Ralph Nader took up the cudgels in a new attack on the recalcitrance of US industries and authorities. Wrapped in complacency only a few months earlier, they began suddenly to drag stringent permissible limits out of the air whether these were practical, meaningful or not.

Entrenched complacency is liable to turn into transient panic when its dereliction is unmasked, and it seems that the way of authority is to let things run on until people or animals begin to fall down. Yet the spectres behind the surge of activity in the US and Canada are, in spite of later whitewashing as reaction to initial overstatement, both real and terrible. By 1968 Dr Karl Rosen who, with Löfroth, was in at the outset of the Swedish investigation at Stockholm University (but at this time was a visiting fellow at the University of Illinois), published with his Canadian colleagues an elegant elucidation and confirmation of the natural methylation of mercury in aquatic systems. Pointing to the action already taken in Japan and Sweden to reduce mercury contamination the authors said flatly that these 'should be followed elsewhere before ... methyl mercury is being titrated in humans as well as fish.'[9]

Coupled with renewed evidence of the highly mutagenic properties of alkyl mercury, and evidence from
Sweden that confirmed the Minamata finding of the
tendency for alkyl mercury to concentrate in the foetus,
the most sinister aspect of the mercury problem was now
seen as the massive iceberg of long-term potential damage
sitting below the surface of inland waters. The markedly
differing symptoms and degree of severity of impairment
suffered by the Huckleby children confirmed the wide
range of sensitivity in the population and the special
vulnerability of children, while the Swedish analyses (FIG.
2:2) suggested that there was a rapid rise in foetal
mercury concentrations at quite low intakes by the
mother.

Again it was seen that, as measured in river and lake
waters, a variation of only a few parts per billion in
concentration of mercury could lead to potentially lethal
concentrations in fish. Worse perhaps, not only was the
extent of contamination unknown but the techniques for
detecting it were difficult because organic mercury is all
too easy to lose in an analytical system. In any case few
executive authorities at that time possessed either the
equipment or the expertise to carry out rapid and
extensive surveys. This is as true of Europe as of North
America at this time and the violent activity in the US,
far from being panic as it has since been described, was
really an indication that the full and very unpleasant
implications were finally being grasped.

DOUBTS AND DOSES

It has been suggested that the highlighting of the
mercury problem, like that of some other heavy metal
contamination problems, is more a reflection of advances
in analytical technique than of real environmental
danger. This is just about as far from the truth as you
can get. The analytical techniques serve to reduce the
uncertainties in environmental problems. (To some

people, of course, uncertainties are valuable because they leave plenty of latitude either for inaction or for profligate activity or, indeed, for criticism.) In the case of mercury, the uncertainties and areas of sheer ignorance are enor-

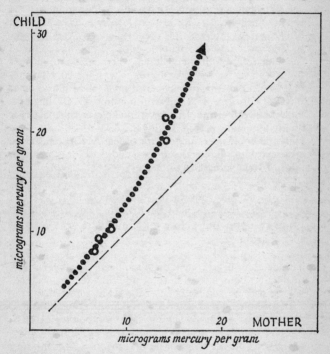

FIG 2:2. Marked tendency for organic mercury to accumulate selectively in the foetus as shown by Swedish analyses of tissue from new-born infants and their mothers. Derived from Löfroth 'Methylmercury', Swedish Natural Science Research Council.

mous. No one knows how mercury damages cells, what the threshold (if any) of cell damage is or what range of sensitivity exists in human beings. Take, for example, the two best determinations of the maximum allowable daily intake (ADI) that, according to scientists at Oak

Ridge National Laboratory, have been made on the scanty information so far available.

In a study of persons with a high intake of Swedish fish contaminated to varying degrees with methylmercury, it was calculated that one subject consumed approximately 150 grams of fish per day with an average mercury concentration of 6·7 ppm wet weight; this is equivalent to 1·0 milligrams of mercury a day. A mercury level of 1·2 ppm in red blood cells was found in this individual, which is about half that found as average for several groups with mercury poisoning. Clinical investigation revealed no signs of illness or of physical impairment. A daily consumption of 1·0 milligrams a day thus represents the highest intake ever calculated for an asymptomatic person. Taking this as a 'no-effect' dose in man and applying a safety factor of ten (which seems to be customary for 'unintentional food additives') this yields an ADI of 100 micrograms of mercury.[10]

There are so many holes in that calculation that it is about as effective as would be a herring net in trying to capture shrimps. But before taking it apart, let's look at determination No 2.

The metabolism and retention of radioactive methylmercury nitrate has been studied in three adult males. The material was seen to be completely absorbed. Measurements made with a whole-body counter over a period of 7 months and corrected for isotope decay indicated a physiological half-life of 70–74 days, equivalent to a daily excretion of 1·0% of the body burden. (Similar results are found if the mercury is bound to food protein.) Radioactivity was also measured over different parts of the body by scintillation scanning and was found to be mainly localized over the liver area with 10–20% in the brain area. The amount of mercury in the brain that causes toxicity has been calculated as 12 milligrams. If this amount of mercury in the brain is assumed to represent 10–20% of the body burden, the total body burden would be 60–120 milligrams. With a daily excretion of 1% the dose of methylmercury needed to maintain equilibrium would be 0·6 to 1·2 milligrams a day. Taking this as a minimum toxic chronic dose to adult man and applying a safety factor of 10, the ADI comes out at 0·06–0·12 milligrams of mercury, i.e. 60 to 120 micrograms.[11]

The first point about determination No 1 is that a single adult example is a poor basis for any calculation covering the whole spectrum of the population. Any standard has to embrace the most sensitive sectors. Further, there is no indication of the duration of exposure of the 'no-effect' individual. In setting permissible limits exposure for an entire lifetime is involved, not one of a few weeks or months. It might be argued that a safety factor of 10 covers possible variations but, if the growing child is, say, twice as sensitive as is an adult to methylmercury, the safety factor is only 5. Furthermore, as the Oak Ridge scientists point out, the estimate is based on the end point of clinically observable damage to the nervous system. Carcinogenic, mutagenic, foetal and very long-term effects, such as the earlier onset of mental senility, are not taken into account.

The second determination may be even less reliable. It is based on a single dose of methylmercury and assumes that the half-life for organic mercury is the same for all organs in the body. There is evidence that the brain half-life is longer than the whole-body average which means that in the real situation of chronic exposure the proportion in the brain will increase with time until a stable plateau is reached. Further, the *assumption* that 12 milligrams (i.e. 40 micrograms per gram) represents a brain-burden threshold at which clinically evident toxicity appears, is not supported by unambiguous evidence. The onset of symptoms has also been calculated to occur at 20 micrograms per gram and at between 3 and 66 micrograms per gram of brain tissue.[12] Again, there is ample evidence to suggest that the metabolism of mercury in infants and children is unlike that of adults and that to be prudent it may be best to assume them to be twice as sensitive as adults. As before, mutagenic and other long term effects are not considered.

So, if there is to be a safety factor of 10, what ADIs do we get if we assume the worst, namely a 20 microgram per gram threshold in the adult brain and double sensitivity in children?[13] The answer, 15–30 micrograms a day, *is within the range of the normal daily intake from uncontaminated food and leaves no room at all for foods with elevated concentrations of mercury.* Even on the basis of that ADI, very long term effects have not been taken into consideration.

So there is good reason to worry and to get down to some thoroughgoing research aimed at defining the long-term effects left out of these calculations, and also aimed at defining more closely where the threshold of damage in the brain lies. Since it seems most probable that brain cells are knocked out one by one by enzymic interference, it may turn out that only a few molecules of methyl-mercury are needed to destroy a cell. Possibly, mercury combines selectively with particular locations on DNA or inhibits ribosomal activity. But the most important thing of all is, in the first place, to track sources of mercury and eliminate them as far as possible.

THE BATTLE

Very properly this was the immediate route embarked upon in the US and Canada where intensified investigation led, by the end of 1970, to the banning of fishing not only in Lake St Clair and Lake Erie, but Lake Champlain, the Saskatchewan River, Lake Winnipeg, the Winnipeg River, Lake Onandaga and, as an advisory measure, in almost 100 rivers. US Government action had by this time, through the establishment of new water standards and threats of legal action, reduced the known overall direct discharges of mercury into freshwaters from 287 lb a day to about 40 lb. Some 50 firms, many of them major, were listed as 'polluters of rivers, streams and lakes.' In Britain such precipitate action sounds like an unnecessary witch-hunt, for slow persuasion has been the rule for almost a century. But Canada followed suit for, as is now recognized, even 40 lb of mercury a day can in the end be locally disastrous. In the main, North American industry remained wisely quiescent, but when the Government of Ontario sued Dow Chemical Co of Canada for 35 million dollars for losses resulting from mercury contamination of the St Clair river and Lake Erie, Dow Chemicals hit back.

They were able to do so because of genuine uncertainties. It was not us, they pleaded in a preliminary suit, but Wyandotte Chemicals, Detrex Chemicals, General Electric Chemical and a dozen others, including the National Aeronautics and Space Administration's Research Center at Lewis, Cleveland, and the fossil fuel users like Detroit Edison and the gas companies.[14] The truth is that up to 1970 the effluent situation and other potential mercury sources had been so inadequately monitored that data essential to a proven allocation of blame would have been hard to find. The only places in which the record was indelibly etched were the sediments of rivers and lakes, where it will still be wielding a disruptive effect on freshwater life in ten years time. Whether the uncertainties will be legally resolved, except to the financial benefit of the legal profession, is less important for the future than that the uncertainties existed at all. These, as well as the bulk of mercury discharges, need to be eliminated.

However, while the tort-masters were limbering up for courtroom gymnastics, environmental scientists of the world converged on Rome for a massive Food and Agricultural Organization technical conference on marine pollution. On December 4 1970, in the week before his departure to Rome, as a kind of preliminary firework for the explosions likely to follow, Prof. B. McDuffie of New York State University rocked public health officials in New York by announcing that canned tuna fish contained up to 0·86 ppm mercury. Since public health authorities had been looking for mercury in foodstuffs for the best part of a year but not finding any, and since the official limit for mercury in foodstuffs had been set at 0·5 ppm, the public health authorities were caught, to put it mildly, in an embarrassing position. Worse, a hasty investigation by the US Federal Drug Administration revealed that some cans of tuna contained more than 1·0 ppm, that some 900 million cans of tuna put on the market that year were probably contaminated to levels above the official limit, and that the mercury levels of canned swordfish were considerably higher than those of tuna.

Remembering that a meal of fish containing 1·0 ppm of mercury means an intake of around 200 micrograms of mercury, while the best rough determinations of a safe ADI give figures around 100 micrograms a day, and that in the US tuna is widely eaten and quite often forms the major part of slimming diets, the authorities were constrained to act. Vast quantities of tuna were abruptly and expensively banned. European authorities, no less taken aback by the finding, for earlier routine analyses had indicated that deep sea fish were relatively uncontaminated, convened hasty meetings. Tuna was examined and, at least in Britain, found to contain comparable quantities of mercury to the US varieties. The public was advised, for the moment, not to eat it. But Britain, in the best traditions of pragmatism, avoids setting official limits and in spite of finding a significant proportion of cans contaminated to levels above 0·5 ppm, contrived to rationalize a course of inaction by resorting to averages. By counting British heads and the number of cans sold a year, and by completely ignoring those who like tuna and eat a lot, the scientific advisory committee was able to arrive at reassuring conclusions.

After a debate which, in the British press during the middle of December, had become vitriolic in its attack on the authorities, and after a spate of mercury-orien-

tated TV programmes in which the gloomy tidings of
Rome appeared most often to be voiced by the bearded
McDuffie, the British Minister of Agriculture, Mr James
Prior, made his announcement in a statement issued by
the Ministry on December 22 1970.

> The experts consider that it is the total intake of methyl
> mercury that is important ... they consider that it is un-
> necessary at this time to withdraw from sale or to advise
> consumers not to eat any of the canned tuna now on the
> market. The tests have shown that all this fish is within the
> safety limit set in some other countries including Sweden.
> In short, there is no reason why the housewife should not
> buy it.

To the credit of the British canning industry the
largest canners, John West, had sidestepped the official
survey and set up its own batch monitoring system. It
found very little mercury, called in the Government
Chemist as advisor, and still found little mercury. But,
in the Minister's statement there as a kind of backward
half-look behind the reassurance. 'There is evidence that
in this country the amount of mercury in the diet is
extremely low. The experts advise me that I should
initiate extensive monitoring [what did the WHO say in
1967?] for all possible sources of methyl mercury intake
including fish.'

So the whole statement was threadbare and devious.
The experts said that it was the 'total intake' that
mattered, but lacked the detailed information to assess it.
'Total' is, in any case, a bad word in the methylmercury
context for it is the repetitive individual's daily dose that
matters, not some notional national average. Why
authorities continue to cling to averages is totally
baffling. It is peaks which matter. If it takes 40 milligrams
of mercury to kill and I get 40 milligrams while you get
none, according to the average we are both safe. But I
will be dead. Incidentally, although he mentioned
Sweden specifically, the Minister failed to point out that

the Swedish limit applied to fish eaten only once a week. The omission looked, and will always look, oddly convenient.

One of the intractable problems, however, posed by the discovery of high mercury levels in tuna was whether its origin was natural or man-created. Like several problems this formed one of the unresolved talking points of the Rome conference. Yet on January 16 1971 it seemed as if the British Medical Journal had made up its mind. 'The methyl mercury recently . . . found in canned tuna,' it declared in a leading article, 'is not of human manufacture.' As it turned out this was not a deduction based on evidence that had eluded the Rome experts, but a revelation that the BMJ had caught up with the findings of 1967—that mercury could be methylated in the environment. On the sources of mercury the BMJ remained uncommitted. It did say without real supporting evidence that 'there is certainly an amount of methyl mercury which can be consumed regularly without producing damage,' adducing industrial expert opinion that this amount might be 100 micrograms a day. Whether this industrial adult figure would be right for non-industrial children was not questioned. 'While it is certainly safe to eat 220 grams of tuna containing 0·5 ppm methyl mercury daily,' it asserted, '*there is at present little information on the margin of safety*.' [My italics]

What an extraordinary statement: if you do not know the margin of safety then you cannot possibly know that something is 'certainly' safe. You may perhaps say that, on the basis of occupational exposure, something 'appears' to be safe for whole populations, but you need to add that, in general, occupational exposures involve the acceptance of risks that are an order of magnitude greater than those properly acceptable for the public at large. The convenient omission of any mention of the genetic, mutagenic and other long-term risks by then known to be at least potentially associated with methyl mercury, and the absence of a discussion of the high vulnerability of children, renders the article suspect. If the Ministry of Agriculture and Fisheries had written the leader in support of its own actions, as some cynics have suggested, it could hardly have designed a more convenient form of special pleading.

FACTS AND FACTORS

Yet, while in Britain and the US, the official and medical establishment viewpoints had not brought the mercury problem into sharp focus even by the end of the 'seventies, there were continual rumblings of serious concern in the scientific community long before then. The establishment in Britain of a standing Royal Commission on Environmental Pollution in February 1970 was the outcome of pressure coming primarily from the public and scientific sectors, as were the establishment of the Central Unit on Environmental Pollution as part of the British Cabinet 'think-tank' and the Environment Protection Agency as a force to be reckoned with in Washington. In Europe the fears which underlay these moves were, from the marine point of view, summed up in quietly academic terms at a Royal Society marine pollution study group meeting in London in December 1969. Pesticides received their due attention, but the largest new worries centred on heavy metals and on the ability of marine animals to concentrate them in unknown ways.

Concentration factors range from less than 1·0 for some metals, such as sodium, to *greater than a million* in the case of zinc and some other heavy metals. In general the concentrations of metals in seawater itself are so low that they can easily be increased a hundred times or more by the pollution of estuaries and inshore waters. In organisms at the lowest end of the life chain the metals are often absorbed and concentrated directly from the water, but these changes can again be magnified by accumulation on specific (and at the moment unknown) routes up the food chain, bringing in their train ecological changes which are at present entirely unpredictable. Potentially these could lead to the disruption of the whole structure of marine life. The ingredients are those of a marine 'Silent Spring' because the situation is complicated not only by the intricate dynamics of water movement and mixing, but by the complex chemistry and biochemistry of metals in water and marine animal metabolism. The form in which a metal occurs, the absence or presence of other and possibly potentiating agents and the metabolic capabilities of individual organisms from microbes to the largest fish species, are all important in determining the outcome when pollution occurs.

This 1969 meeting amounted, then, to confirmation of a most disturbing situation. Leading experts were saying that they possessed nothing like the knowledge needed to interpret or to predict pollution effects. (While, in areas of research of less public importance, cynical observers comment that in the search for funds scientists are apt to point out goals of great value sitting just over the horizon of current knowledge, the fabric of knowledge about marine pollution was too fragmental to reveal even the most important threads to follow.) True, during the period from 1930 onward, a great deal of research had gone into the study of metal toxicity but this had been aimed at the production of anti-fouling materials for ships and marine structures. It was concerned with the direct effects of metals in high concentrations. Chronic effects at low concentrations had hardly been studied at all. Once again events had run far ahead of the knowledge needed to ensure safety.

At Rome all these uncertainties, the lack of knowledge and the immense areas of uncertainty attended by spectres of global marine disaster were re-emphasized on a fully international basis. It happened that the conference met in the shadow of a very significant laboratory finding. Since one immediate concern about marine pollution is the possible loss of fishery production, scientists at Florida State University took a quick look at the effects of organic mercury compounds on the growth of the basic foodstuff of the seas and freshwaters: phytoplankton. A major factor limiting the total productivity of the earth is the efficiency with which energy from the sun can be converted into materials which higher animals use as food. Just as the fate of land creatures depends on the abundance of naturally or agriculturally produced plants, so do the larger creatures of the sea depend on plankton. The Florida State University findings were startling and, implicitly at least, somewhat frightening.[15]

It was found that at concentrations of only 1 part per *billion* or less, organic mercurials reduced photosynthetic efficiency by 50% (FIG. 2:3). In other words concentrations of mercury at levels well below those considered in relation to fish toxicity, and well below those being imposed for even human drinking water standards, could have dramatic and damaging effects on the basic mechanisms of marine life. *The sensitivity of the aquatic life system is far greater than has, in the past, been imagined by even the most extreme environmental pessimists.* No direct interpretation may be possible from this single finding, for there are many factors—such as temperature and the availability of suitable nutrients—which also limit productivity, but the implications are very serious.

Curiously and dangerously, there was an argument propagated at this time that the amount of mercury that has accumulated *naturally* in sea water is so massive when compared to man's contribution (35 million tons compared to an annual input of 15 thousand tons) that it was false, misleading and dangerously alarmist to pretend that heavy metal marine pollution was of sufficient magnitude to even begin to interfere with the life systems of the ocean. Those who put this argument forward, and those who pointed out the large naturally occurring unevenness in deep oceanic concentrations of mercury, fell into what were, by then, familiar traps.

Taken as an average over the whole volume of the ocean man's contribution of heavy metals may well be insignificant. In the case of mercury it has been calculated, for example, that it would take 2000 years at present rates of mercury contamination for the ocean concentration to

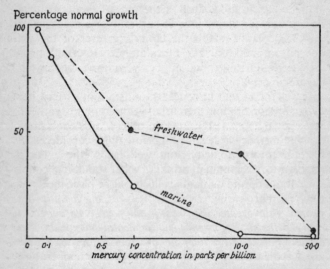

Percentage normal growth

mercury concentration in parts per billion

FIG 2:3. Dramatic reduction of growth of freshwater phytoplankton and a species of marine diatom at very low concentrations of methyl mercury dicyandiamide. Measured by photosynthetic uptake of radio-carbon. A logarithmic horizontal scale is used to reveal the effects of concentrations below one part per billion. (Derived from Harriss, White and Macfarlane, 1971.)

double. Such calculations are not merely abstract and simplistic, but can be dangerously misleading. It takes tens of thousands of years for metallic marine pollutants to disperse uniformly: contamination therefore builds up in those waters into which pollutants are discharged, in this case estuaries, coastal areas and nearby shallow continental shelf areas. Because these areas are also the most highly productive of the entire oceans, the dangers are real and immense. Relatively small quantities of contaminants can disrupt the life processes in the sea's most important areas and may already be doing so.

This, then, was the spectre which led to Rome and which was there confirmed in paper after paper that, outlining fragmental knowledge, revealed clearly the gaps which urgently required filling. In a classic document summarizing the situation Prof. J. K. Meittinen of Helsinki University and Dr S. Keckes of the International Atomic Energy Laboratory of marine radiobiology[16] pointed out how little was known about the effects of mercury on lower marine organisms, but what *was* known suggested an enormous range of possible effects, even from exposure to very low concentrations. In particular the need to consider teratogenic (effects on the developing organism) and genetic effects, as well as direct toxicity, on the whole spectrum of marine organisms, was given emphasis, as was the need to know a great deal more about possible potentiating effects between the many heavy metals.

What happens when there is not only mercury present in abnormally high concentration (high in relation to the normal seawater concentrations that is, but not necessarily by more than a few parts per billion) but also lead, and copper and zinc and any of the many metals now common as contaminants? This is an immensely complex biological problem which is only fragmentally answered (in relation to those metals which are important as animal *nutrients*), but which has hardly been studied in relation to low level contamination and chronic toxicity. The general rule appears to be that, although some metals will counteract the effects of others, when heavy metals work together their combined effect is greater than that expected from simple addition. Synergisms, as these magnified or potentiated effects are called, have been a dominant worry in the background of environmental research for many years, but remarkably little is known about them. Lack of financial support, the nature of scientific research itself—which to produce understandable results necessarily limits the number of variables in an experimental situation—and the distorting effects of technological commitment which tends to emphasize the positive rather than the negative aspects of development, have all helped to maintain a shroud of ignorance.

Yet, by the time this conference took place, an abundance of uncorrelated information had been collected, mainly as a result of sudden environmental concern. An examination of 81 marine species off the Californian coast revealed concentrations of mercury ranging from 0·4 to 21 ppm (dry weight). Methyl mercury was shown to possess a half-life in freshwater mussels of up to 435 days, while bacteria and other microbes were shown not only to transform inorganic into organic mercury but to fix it, concentrate it and in some cases, cause increased volatilization of sedimentary deposits. Further, the initial demonstration of microbial methylation of mercury in anaerobic conditions had been re-examined and found to be only partly true. In some conditions, anaerobic or not, methylation occurred but, even in anaerobic conditions, would not occur rapidly if the mercury was in the form of the sulphide H_2S. All these factors point toward enormous complexity resulting from variations in water conditions, sediment conditions and the biological mechanisms of different creatures. In eggs, some kinds of mercury concentrate in the yolk, some in the white: some produce deformities, others do not. But the amounts of mercury involved in the disruption of normal biological processes need only be small, for (in marine species as in mammals) various mercurials tend to concentrate in different organs so that, in food chain accumulation, dramatic and quite unpredictable effects can occur.

ACTION AND REACTION

So the Rome Conference, having revealed the implications and the lack of adequate knowledge about marine as well as freshwater mercury pollution, went to town on recommendations—yet again—of international monitoring systems, the prohibition of ocean-dumping of toxic wastes and, quite specifically, the recommendation of Government action to render mandatory 'advanced techniques for mercury recovery in all factories producing mercurial products or using mercury or its compounds as catalysts, cathodes or other purposes in production'. The reduction of mercurial use in countries like Japan, Sweden and the US was not enough. Much closer control and, as far as possible, the elimination of mercury from discharges was recommended as a matter of urgency.

But, while the implications of the Rome meeting were being absorbed by the environmental advisory systems of the participating countries, public reaction to what was believed to be overstatement of the mercury problem was already evident. In North America, under headings like 'The Great Mercury Mistake', the importance of the discoveries of 10 years was being minimized in the popular press. The finding, for example, that mercury levels in cereals—although patchy—were low, was taken as a general indicator that things were better than had seemed possible only a year earlier. Further, industries using mercury were making and broadcasting discoveries about possible agents to reduce the effects of organic mercury poisoning in mammals. That these were, to put it mildly, premature, that environmentally they were irrelevant, that the environmental problems still remained unmapped and that, as investigations went on, even higher levels of mercury were being found in some animals, are facts which seem to have been overlooked. Because it aims at high impact the press inevitably swings from extreme to extreme and, although it can be fairly claimed that the public media played an important role in stimulating concern over mercury contamination, it has done little to help elucidate in the public mind the real complexity, extent and seriousness of the problem.

The question of acceptable levels for the public, for

example, in addition to the ADIs calculated at Oak
Ridge and elsewhere, had been examined in a number of
countries on the basis of mercury levels in human hair.
It is one of the characteristics of metals that they bind
very firmly to the forming keratin of hair, and it is generally believed that hair provides a kind of organic record
of blood-metal levels. In forensic science the technique is
used in hair identification and in the confirmation of metal
poisoning and, some years ago in England, it might be
remembered that an analysis of Napoleon's hair led to
the suggestion that he had been poisoned with arsenic on
Elba! Well, mercury builds up in hair in the same way,
and the examination of hair-mercury levels of people at
Minamata, Niigata and in Sweden and Finland led to
some rough conclusions about the hair levels that related
to clinical levels of poisoning.

The application of hair-metal levels as an index of
exposure rests on an assumed direct relationship between
blood-metal levels and hair-metal levels induced at the
time of growth. In Japan, among those suffering severe
clinical poisoning, the mercury in hair ranged from 60
to 530 ppm but it is generally believed that the figures are
unreliable and probably much too low. Although the
wide scatter of concentrations is also present in Swedish
and Finnish investigations, it is generally *assumed* that
hair level indicating clinical toxicity is about 150 ppm.
In Sweden the highest adult levels among fish-eaters
turned out to be around 8 ppm, while in Finland these
reached 30 ppm. (In one case a level of 180 ppm was
found.) Now the 'normal' level in adult populations is
between 1·0 and 4·0 ppm, so it is clear that in Sweden and
Finland blood-mercury levels had been considerably
elevated. In the absence of clinical symptoms and with
no records of foetal damage, this is taken as an indication
that no human harm was done. Yet, when New York
State University carried out a short-sharp hair-level
survey among tuna eaters in 1970–71 it found hair-
mercury levels ranging from 8·0 to 43·0 ppm, that is up

to 15 times the average level of the control sample of the general population and comparable to levels found in 'affected' fish eaters in Sweden. Yet these were not people feeding from a locally contaminated lake.

Since the amount of mercury laid down in hair seems to vary widely between individuals you might take the 43 ppm either as an indication of an unusually high rate of incorporation or as an indication that blood-mercury level had, in fact, been even higher than the figure suggests. But even on its face value it indicates an exposure to mercury that is abnormally high, at least one third of the way along the route to clinical poisoning. In a foetus from such a parent blood-mercury levels around the half-way point to clinical poisoning might be expected, a situation that no toxicologist would regard as 'acceptable'. This not only emphasizes the potential seriousness of contamination even at the low levels experienced in tuna, but raises important questions about the reliability of the criteria used in determining whether or not current whole-population exposures are 'safe'.

The problem is not only that the borderline between 'safe' and 'unsafe' is extremely small but that it may vary widely between individuals and be significantly affected by the presence or absence of other contaminants. Some shampoos and hairdressings contain mercurials while others affect absorption. Since mercury uptake by the hair also varies from individual to individual and not necessarily in any constant relationship to mercury sensitivity, this means that although in any single individual it may provide a useful index of exposure, it is an unreliable index for whole-population exposures in the context of standards and public health. It is used, and indeed was used in Britain at the time of the tuna affair, because it was the best index available. But it is not good enough, for it could minimize danger.

Those seeking to do this have, for example, repeatedly drawn attention to evidence that the levels of mercury in marine and freshwater fish of 50 or 100 years ago (sampled from museums) were similar to those being found today. Quite apart from the possibility of contamination during preservation processes, this is neither wholly true nor genuinely relevant. Peak levels of more than 1·0 ppm (wet weight equivalent) have been found for preserved freshwater fish, but no levels approaching the Swedish, Finnish and Canadian peaks of the late 'sixties have been revealed. Further, unreliable evidence from the past is quite irrelevant to modern public health. What we need to know is whether current levels are of significance and, if they are, how they can be controlled.

SCATTERED WARNINGS

The Rome conference unmasked one of the looming difficulties. Marine animals, living in apparently similar and relatively uncontaminated areas, have a curious and unexplained wide range of metal concentrations. This point, which may well be of great importance in future legislation and control (for it implies a need to be extremely strict), was also brought to light in Britain during an investigation of the death of high numbers of seal pups off the Cornish coast.[17] Although it was concluded that the separation of unweaned pups from parents because of unusually bad weather was the prime cause of death, heavy metal analyses of the dead pups and of a control group from a colony off the Northeast coast revealed some unexplained anomalies.

Arsenic levels in liver and kidney, for example, ranged from less than 1·0 ppm to over 50 ppm. In some animals the level was much higher in the kidney than in the liver, while in others the reverse was found. There was, in general, much more lead in the tissue of the northern pups, but the Cornish pups were unexpectedly rich in mercury. Kidney and liver levels ranged up to 13 ppm, sufficiently high to trigger a further investigation. The point is that both colonies, although coastal, are in areas substantially remote from known sources of contamination.

Similar, but even more scattered findings, emerged from a later but very much more extensive investigation following the death of an estimated 50,000 to 100,000 seabirds, mainly guillemots, in the Irish Sea in the autumn of 1969. The full report did not emerge from Britain's Natural Environment Research Council, which had co-opted the resources of a host of laboratories for the work, until the spring of 1971. Preliminary reports, indicating unexplained starvation in the birds and implicating unusually high levels of PCBs (industrial polychlorinated-biphenyls) whose action is similar to that of organochlorine pesticides, as a contributory cause of weakness, were confirmed in the final reports.[18] But by then comprehensive analyses for nine heavy metals had been completed, and these contained some strange and potentially serious anomalies.

First, although lead levels in general were around 5·0 ppm (dry weight) in kidney and liver, in some samples these reached 40·0 ppm (dw). Mercury distribution was even stranger: while half the birds had organs containing less than 0·1 ppm (dw), several reached levels above 3·0 ppm and one contained 23·0 ppm—perhaps close to a lethal level. This scatter was not explicable by variations in water concentrations or in the normal food chains of the birds. It still remains mysterious. But it led the investigators, whose work was collated and edited by Dr Martin Holdgate—head of the British Government's Central Unit on Environmental Pollution—to conclude that heavy metal poisoning could not be ruled out as one of the contributory factors in this massive slaughter of seabirds.

Since both antimony and cadmium had also been found at unexpectedly high concentrations in some of the birds, there was again a hint that this 'natural' disaster was, in reality, the result of complex interacting but debilitating contamination effects which, when the birds were challenged by moderately harsh conditions, left them too weak to survive. The significant environmental point is that *without the presence of high natural stress the effects of scattered marine contamination do not show*. It is therefore quite wrong-headed to think in terms of single contaminants when considering effects on ecosystems, for it is the combined interaction of many sublethal effects which matters. When natural conditions swing to extremes then whole populations, not just a few weak individual animals, are likely to collapse.

Mercury, however, presents special problems and deserves individual detailed attention. Looking for industrial sources, Sweden rapidly pinpointed the so-called chloralkali industry which, increasingly, is making use of large plants. In these a recycled mercury catalyst is employed to convert a feedstock of common salt (NaCl) into caustic soda (sodium hydroxide: NaOH) and chlorine. Most of the large plants are 'in-house' operations of very large chemical groups, requiring the products as feedstock in bleaching, detergent manufacture, plastics, pesticides and many other products and functions. Throughout the world this kind of plant is increasing in capacity at a rate of 7–10% per annum. A single mercury cell requires about 1500 lb of catalyst for each ton of daily chlorine capacity, and the daily capacities of the US and Britain are now running, respectively, at around 8000 and 2000 tons of chlorine. So there is an enormous amount of mercury in use in these industries alone. What is even more significant is that an overall mercury loss of about 0·5 lb per ton of chlorine produced was regarded as industrially 'acceptable' right up to 1969. In Britain losses of this order were still accepted in 1971.[19] The products themselves, chlorine and caustic soda, are necessarily contaminated with mercury and therefore add to the industrial and environmental burdens.

LOSSES AND LOOPHOLES

What seems strangely remiss is that, although the Swedes and some East European countries took a hard look at the chlor-alkali industry back in the mid-'sixties, the US did not follow until 1970 and, as far as could be seen, Britain had still taken no special measures by 1971. Certainly at that time the mercury cell loss experienced in the processes employed by the largest single British producer, ICI, were informally confirmed as around 0·5 lb per ton of chlorine.

That is not, of course, the amount of mercury reaching rivers from these plants. In the main it is run into settling ponds and allowed to collect. What happens after that remains something of a mystery. A process sometimes used by DuPont in the US is that of drying and combustion (where does it fall-out?). Some mercury may well be dumped in the oceans, and use is also made of 'spreading on waste land so that the mercury weathers away.' Quite obviously there is considerable latitude here for serious contamination and, as the Oak Ridge laboratory has pointed out, there is in fact no need at all for such large industrial losses. Potentially these amount to around 500 tons in the US and perhaps 150 tons in the UK, quantities which are comparable to the amount of mercury released as vapour in the burning of fossil fuels.

But, by early 1970, it had been shown if not implemented, that the losses from mercury cell chlor-alkali plants could be reduced to 1% of present levels if more efficient recovery and recycling techniques were used. Since mercury costs about £1 a lb ($2.40/lb) this might seem worthwhile—without consideration of ultimate environmental effects. With the extensive problems of the long life of mercury in contaminated areas already all too evident, the case for reducing discharges to an absolute minimum seems irrefutable. Indeed, any continuance of present loss levels is like to be viewed by future generations as a characteristically irresponsible act condoned by

our economically dominated and environmentally profligate society. It may be very significant that in US
industrial loss analyses (Britain had published none by
mid-1971), the potential losses of mercury through the
hydrogen condensate of these plants was not even
mentioned. Yet about half the total loss can occur by that
route, with another large proportional loss in brine
sludge. Both can be virtually eliminated.

Britain's fragmented regulatory systems and long
tradition of concealment of industrial data has produced
a situation in which it is virtually impossible to carry out
an overall assessment of the contribution of particular
processes to environmental contamination. In the case
of the chlor-alkali process, for example, the chlorine part
of the process comes under the Alkali Inspectorate and
the Factory Inspectorate, but nobody seems to be responsible for stack losses of mercury. While the river
authorities are concerned (with local authorities) in the
granting of permission for discharges into streams and
rivers, the creation of settling ponds and the fate of
materials spread or dumped *appears* to be covered by
general 'nuisance' laws which were neither designed to
deal with industrial waste nor appropriate to highly
persistent contaminants. The 'nuisance' has to be
demonstrated before it can be stopped! And, in the case
of surface contamination by heavy metals, whose ultimate fate it is impossible to determine (although under-
ground aquifers and agriculture can well be affected),
control is essential from the outset. The loopholes are
large and all tend to favour industrial laxity.

Indeed the growing relative laxity of Britain's industrial
control of mercury is demonstrated by a comparison of
present standards for maximum allowable concentrations
(MAC values) for mercury in different countries. While
the US still had no official 'standards' in 1971, the recommended MAC values for occupational exposure were 100
micrograms per cu metre (inorganic) and 10 micrograms
per cu metre (organic). Russia allows only 10 micrograms

per cu metre and 5 micrograms per cu metre, respectively. West Germany, perhaps well ahead of other European countries in its awareness of chemical mutagen problems, permits only 1 microgram per cu metre. Britain, seemingly still back in the 'thirties, lays a blanket MAC value of 100 micrograms per cu metre, in spite of recent international recommendations indicating that this is far too lax for organic mercurials. In practice, humans are in fact officially excluded from organic mercurial processes in Britain, but there appear to be no figures on the efficiency of plant design, the criteria for maintenance storage and handling atmospheres, or on the amounts of organic vapour which reach local external environments.

Yet rough estimates suggest that, with British chloralkali capacity now around 800,000 tons a year and mercury losses running at about 0·5 lb per ton, 150 to 200 tons of mercury a year are reaching the environment from this source *alone*. Similar losses are probably occurring in France, Germany and several other heavily industrialized countries, while the losses in the United States are potentially four or five times larger. In the West, as in Japan, plastics factories may be creating serious local mercury 'hot spots' which, so far, have gone unnoticed and, although examination of the situation may reveal that in fact losses and contamination levels are lower than might be expected, there are good grounds for ensuring open public scrutiny.

While in these cases most of the mercury will be in settling ponds (from which presumably it could be recovered) there may also be large non-recoverable emissions of mercury vapour from many industrial sources. Mercury is present in significant quantities in fossil fuels and, although in the case of natural gas the environment is protected by the accidental precipitation of mercury as a sulphide in pipelines, most of the mercury in coal—which in Britain may be 3000 to 10,000 tons a year and in the US as much as 40,000 tons—may well be pumped straight out of stacks. We need to know what the quantities are, how the vapour falls-out, and what controls can be applied. No less urgently, we need to know whether other industries—smelting for example —are adding significantly to environmental and human burdens of the metal. Any measure which reduces these burdens must be regarded as good.

Once heavily contaminated, sediments and surface areas are difficult if not impossible to clean up. Suggested measures, such as dredging sediments (and presumably dumping them elsewhere) or covering them with coatings, all involve considerable cost, effort and interference with established life structures. Optimists have proposed the use of shellfish in the mining of metals from sediments— as a cleaning up not an economic operation—and although this would do little damage it would be a long, slow operation whose effectiveness would fall below practical limits long before sediment metal-levels became safe.

A more likely and more sinister possibility is that, with the continuing unrestricted discharge of industrial waste into estuaries and coastal waters, *accidental* mining of metals in shellfish will be one of the routes by which dangerously large amounts of mercury enter the human diet. Coastal and freshwater fish-farming is likely to develop rapidly during the 'seventies and 'eighties, but it may well be that areas otherwise ideal for this desirable advance are already fouled beyond economic recovery. It needs to be remembered that, in Sweden, a lake into which mercury ceased to be dumped in 1945 was still highly contaminated in 1970 and may still be economically worthless at the turn of the century. The movement and self-cleansing action of marine sediments may be much faster, but at the moment far too little is known to make any optimistic predictions about the effects of past industrial discharges.

Yet, whatever the effects of past mistakes, whether humanly tragic or ecologically crippling, the implications of mercurial discharges and the real and potential extent of their effects are at least, and at last, beginning to be understood. Since ours are the generations which have first learned the harsh lessons of the past, it will be our actions and the actions of our Governments and industries, which will be judged by future generations. If the sluggishness of response in Britain, Europe, Japan and North America are an indication of the urgency with which the situation is viewed, we are already open to the harshest of judgements, that of wilful neglect.

EPILOGUE TO CHAPTER TWO

The enormous amount of research necessary to eliminate uncertainties in our present understanding of mercury contamination far outstrips available manpower and other resources. No early solutions to existing problems are likely because of the enormously complex, dynamic structure of the environment. The scientists at Oak Ridge National Laboratory—a laboratory notable for its leanings toward quaint English and the apt quotation—found in 1971 the appropriate words to sum up the situation. In the section given to the criteria for evaluating mercury levels in the ORNL report on mercury in the environment they first defined their criteria as 'an expression of the scientific knowledge of the effects that can be expected to occur whenever the level of a pollutant reaches or exceeds a specific figure.' Appropriately, perhaps, in a Mad Hatter situation, the assessment of present scientific knowledge is left to Alice:

'What do you know about this business?' the king said to Alice.
'Nothing,' said Alice.
'Nothing *whatever?*' persisted the king.
'Nothing whatever,' said Alice.
'That's very important,' said the king, turning to the jury.[20]

It is. The admission of ignorance is more worthy than the concealment of possible environmental effects. It will forever seem unfortunate that mercury contamination publications from official bodies, such as the Fisheries

Research Board of Canada, contrive like British Government statements, to exclude reference to genetic and mutagenic properties of mercury. It is up to the public to draw conclusions about this. Industry will argue that if the public wants better protection then it must pay. This is sheer cynicism. Directly or indirectly the public always pays.

Notes and References

1. A. Jernelov: *Mercury in Freshwater Systems: Progress Reports*, Swedish National Environment Protection Board, 1969.

2. S. Jensen and A. Jernelov: *Nordforsk Biocidinformation* No 10 (1967), p 4.

3. The organic mercury levels at Minamata suggest that either the rate of natural methylation was unusually high or that the amounts of mercury reaching the estuary and sea in the years before 1953 were higher than indicated by the official record.

4. 'Evaluation of the Toxicity of Pesticide Residues in Food,' WHO (Food Additives) No 23 (1964), p 162.

5. G. Löfroth: *Methylmercury*, Swedish Natural Science Research Council: Ecological Research Bulletin No 4, 1969, p 14.

6. Annual Report of the Ministry of Agriculture Research Station, Long Ashton, Bristol, 1959.

7. M. H. Berlin and others: *Archives of Environmental Health*, vol 19: 891, 1969.

8. A popular and lively blow-by-blow account of the political confusion and vacillation over the mercury issue in the US is contained in 'Mercury' by Peter and Katherine Montague (Sierra Club, 1971).

9. J. M. Wood, F. S. Kennedy and C. G. Rosen: *Nature*, vol 220:173, 1968.

10. R. A. Wallace and others: 'Mercury in the Environment: The Human Element,' Oak Ridge National Laboratory report, January 1971, p 25.

11. See reference 10.

12. F. Berglund and M. Berlin: Human risk evaluation for various populations in Sweden due to methylmercury in fish. (Chemical Fallout, Current Research on Persistent Pesticides, published by Charles C. Thomas, 1969.)

13. This figure could still be high. Experimental studies in Japan and Sweden have demonstrated that whole-body concentrations of methylmercury in the range 17–23 micrograms/gram are *fatal* in cats, rats and mice. See, for example, B. Halstead: 'Toxicity of Marine Organisms Caused by Pollution,' a WHO contribution to the 1970 Rome Conference on Marine Pollution (ref: MP/70/R-6, October 9 1970).

14. The legal battle along these lines began in a private action brought against Dow Chemicals Co of Canada by a marine proprietor. See, for example, reports in the *Toronto Telegram* March 22 1971 and onward.

15. R. B. Harriss and others: 'Mercury Compounds reduce Photosynthesis by Plankton,' *Science*, vol 170:736–7, November 13 1970.

16. S. Keckes and J. K. Miettenen: 'Mercury as a Marine Pollutant,' 1970 Rome Conference on Marine Pollution (ref: MP/70/R-26, November 25 1970)

17. W. N. Bonner: 'Seal Deaths in Cornwall,' British Natural Environment Research Council publications, Series C, No 1, 1970.

18. 'The Sea Bird Wreck in the Irish Sea Autumn 1969,' British Natural Environment Research Council publications, Series C, No 4, 1971.

19. No official estimates of losses have been published. Imperial Chemical Industries, a major producer, confirmed in May 1971 that British mercury cell losses were similar to those in the US, about 0·5 lb mercury per ton of chlorine produced.

20. *Alice's Adventures in Wonderland* by Lewis Carroll, Chapter 12.

21. A British Ministry of Agriculture survey of 1971 played down the discovery of three heavily contaminated coastal areas. Flatfish containing mercury up to 2·5 ppm were found in the Thames estuary. (*Report on Mercury in Food: Her Majesty's Stationery Office, October 1971.*)

CHAPTER THREE

OUR DAILY LEAD

Lead is hardly less dangerous than mercury and, in children, is similar in that at low intake levels it can selectively damage the brain. It accumulates in bone even in its inorganic forms and has been shown to be damaging in every biological system in which it has been examined. As a natural component of the earth's crust—averaging about 16 ppm—it is everywhere and has been present since the beginning of life. But the amounts in the soil, the rivers, the rain, the air we breathe and the food we eat and drink are growing insidiously. Unlike mercury, whose annual man-mobilized contribution to the environment is perhaps 3 or 4 times that which occurs naturally, the man-mobilized contribution of lead is massive. Natural lead mobilization amounts to about 150 thousand tons a year: man's activities unleash over *4 million tons a year* (FIG. 3:1). Of this something like a million tons is pumped into the atmosphere by vehicles in the form of fine aerosols which could hardly have been better designed for widespread dispersal, nor indeed better designed to ensure that the lead is readily absorbed by people and the living systems on which they depend.

The pattern of contamination is very complicated. There are many serious sources other than vehicles and the natural cycles into which the lead is taken are themselves complicated. There are variations in absorption rates, between individuals, species, and differing absorption routes. There are differences of toxicity between different compounds of lead. But if you eat lead with your food something like 10% of it will get into your bloodstream: if you inhale it anything from 15% to 70% may be absorbed. So there is plenty of room for controversy, a situation which has been exploited relentlessly by those whose interests lie in the continuation and expansion of established technological practice. With mordant vigour, the situation has also been exploited by those who enjoy kicking the Establishment although, in this case, their action may well be fully justified.

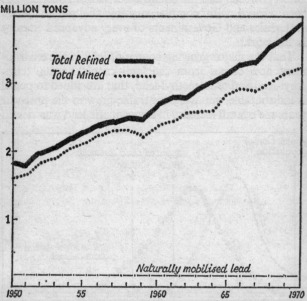

MILLION TONS

Total Refined ▬▬▬
Total Mined ••••••••

Naturally mobilised lead

FIG. 3:1. World production of lead is doubling every 20 years. Already the natural contribution of lead to the environment is negligible compared to that from man-made sources. The total omits lead which is recycled without being re-refined (World Metal Statistics).

Before delving into the complexities of the situation and the controversies that have arisen as a result of differing points of view and differing commitments of those taking part, one important fact needs to be made clear. Of all the known dangerous contaminants of the environments of developed countries, the levels of lead—as measured in the blood of ordinary people—are the highest. Indeed *the range of levels found in urban populations, including children who are probably much more sensitive to lead poisoning than adults, actually overlaps the range known to cause accepted classical symptoms of lead poisoning* (FIG. 3:2). Yet this situation, with the exception of the USSR, Sweden and the countries of North America, has been viewed with complacency by the public health authorities and Governments of every advanced country in the world.

That the major growing source of lead in the environment now comes from the 'anti-knock' agents, tetra-ethyl-lead and tetra-methyl-lead, that are added to petrol is indisputable, yet as motor traffic grew in the post-war years the overall increase in atmospheric lead was viewed

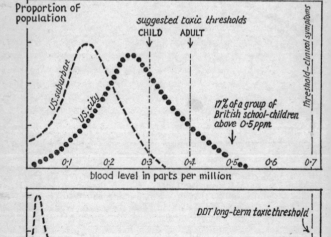

FIG. 3:2. Present levels of lead and DDT in human populations. The blood-lead levels already exceed recently suggested toxic thresholds (data: Philadelphia, 1962) and are approaching the clinical threshold of poisoning. The levels of DDT are relatively much lower. (After Prof. D. Bryce-Smith in *Chemistry in Britain*.)

without much concern because, simultaneously, there was a general reduction of lead from other sources. Incidents of lead poisoning, such as that in Queensland in 1929 when the authorities suddenly became aware of a high incidence of chronic nephritis (damage to kidneys) among children drinking rainwater that had been collected from lead-painted roofs, are bringing about a gradual transition from the use of lead to the use of titanium in paint manufacture. But there have also been extensive cases of lead-poisoning among children in old property where those with the habit of eating non-food fragments (pica) were picking up flakes of lead paint. The problem of pica and of lead ingestion in old properties is by no means resolved and, especially in the United States, is still serious.[1] But this problem is quite separate from that of whole population exposure, except that any lead acquired from one route is added to that picked up from others.

So, while acknowledging that pica presents serious problems in old property areas and that cases of lead poisoning occur in the general population through such incidents as the use of old accumulators as fuel, the central question of lead contamination and of whole-population exposure rests on the routes of ingestion common to everyone—namely food, air and water. Are we consuming more lead from this essential intake than the body's natural detoxification systems can deal with, and at what rate is consumption rising? What are the dangers and which groups of people are most at risk?

ERRORS AND SMEARS

It is commonplace for medical men and toxicologists, including those who have over the years dealt fairly successfully with the problems of lead poisoning in industry, to talk about 'natural' levels of lead in the blood, quoting an 'average' level around 0·2 parts per million. One of the reasons for clinging to this figure is that it has been fairly constant in the scientific literature since serious studies were carried out in the 1930s, during the growth and establishment of the 'anti-knock' lead industry. Quite apart from the danger of leaning on averages, the trouble is that any figures published before the 1960s are probably inaccurate because the analytical techniques were subject to contamination and had large margins of error. In the last four decades, for example, the accepted concentration of lead in ocean water has, through the work of many investigators and of gradually refining techniques, dropped from five micrograms of lead per litre to five-hundredths of a microgram per litre.[2] Quite apart from the massive increases of lead reaching surface waters during that time no scientist would accept this as meaning that the concentrations of lead in sea water had actually declined over the years. Such an interpretation is physically and chemically impossible. The only sensible interpretation is that even the best methods of analysis in the first half of this century gave results which were systematically much too high.

If they were high in geochemistry they were probably high in medicine to a degree which now invalidates them for use in comparative studies. The only reliable way of assessing changes in the background levels of lead over the years is to examine structures of one kind or another in which, layer by layer, the changing concentration in the environment has been recorded. The two best sources are trees, which incorporate environmental lead as they grow and which neatly separate each year's growth so that dating is easy; and polar snow which, falling in a locally uncontaminated region, will contain a record of the yearly concentrations of atmospheric contaminants. By applying the best current analytical techniques a really accurate comparison can be made.

An analysis of the rings of elm trees carried out in 1961[3] provided some evidence of increasing accumulation in recent years. The tree rings of 1900–10 contained

0·12 ppm of lead; those of 1940–7 rather more, 0·33 ppm, and those of 1956–9 showed the much higher value of 0·74 ppm. There is, of course, the possibility that by some unknown mechanism the lead incorporated into each year's growth slowly diffuses out again, and also that with increasing age trees absorb heavy metals at a higher rate in proportion to their size. Neither of these possibilities have been examined but, since both seem unlikely, the best interpretation is that over the years the amount of lead in the environment has increased.

These, as it happens, were urban American trees and therefore liable to be reflecting, not a general increase, but some purely local event. The same criticism cannot, however, apply to Arctic or Antarctic snows which, in a collaborative venture between Japanese and United States scientists, were very carefully examined in 1965 and 1966. The results of the Arctic survey are startling: the concentration of lead, increasing steadily from 1750, takes a sharp upward turn from 1930 onward and is now soaring (FIG. 3:3). The figures also appear to show, and this is an indication of sensitivity, fallout from volcanic eruptions.

This analysis has been criticized ('smeared' might be a better word for the criticism has arisen in the angry debate about the elimination of lead from petrol) on the grounds that the snow samples representing recent years had been contaminated by local expeditionary activity by aircraft and vehicles. It is worth restating the authors' comments on this point:

The Camp Century site (where deep samples were taken) was unsuitable for the collection of recent samples because of contamination at the surface by human activity since 1954 and by partial annual melting. Our party, joined by members of the US Army Research Support Group, therefore embarked from Camp Century in August . . . travelling hundreds of kilometres upwind to a desolate virgin site. There, working parties dug a trench 50 feet deep and 300 feet long to collect samples of snowfalls from the last 15 years.[4]

Not only were the scientists engaged in this survey greatly experienced in environmental studies and therefore at least as aware of the dangers of accidental con-

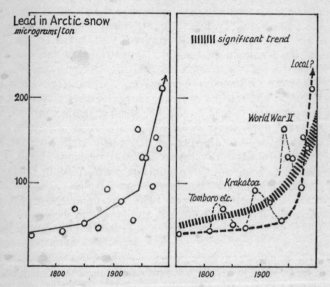

FIG. 3:3. The increasing concentration of lead in Arctic snow. Left: as drawn by the research scientists who carried out the study. Right: interpreted to show correlations between the unevenness of measurements and natural events which might have caused peaks. Even assuming some local contamination after 1954 there is a rapid upward significant trend.

tamination as their critics, but the criticism itself is double-edged. The suggestion that this remote surface has, in recent years, been severely contaminated by the very few overflying petrol-engined aircraft that operate in the area must lead to the conclusion that contamination in other areas is proportionately worse. They cannot have it both ways and, to be honest, the best interpretation is that the samples are truly representative of changes in global lead contamination. The following year, 1966, the findings were backed up by parallel studies in the Antarctic which revealed a much smaller but still measurable increase in contamination over the years. This would be expected for, so far, the Northern Hemisphere has been the dominant region of industrial growth and contamination.

So there is very good reason to believe that, in spite of apparently steady but probably bogus blood-lead levels over the years, the real situation is one in which lead contamination is increasing very rapidly. It is possible to extrapolate backward, working from such information as the calculated input of heavy metals into the oceans from natural sources, to arrive at a picture of contamination levels of surface soils and water in the pre-industrial times in which man evolved. This was done by Dr C. C. Patterson and it turned out that the levels of lead in food and water at that time, excluding local areas where the amount of lead in soils was anomalously high, would result in blood-lead levels of about 0·0025 ppm[5] (see also note 22) almost 100th of those common today.

Since lead has no known natural role in biological processes, but is on the contrary damaging to living things in whatever form it appears, this change can only be for the worse. But, fortunately for man if not for many other living things, he has a kind of in-built series of mechanisms in which are partially protective. In the scientific paper which, working from first principles, he arrived at the extremely low 'natural' level of population exposure to lead, Dr Patterson went on to calculate daily levels of lead from food, water and the atmosphere for urban and country dwellers and concluded that not only did the amount being ingested from the air form a significant fraction of the total, but that the total amounted to 'chronic lead insult' which could, in time, result in serious health hazards.

One of the factors which prompted the extensive survey of the existing literature on lead contamination and toxicology involved in this study was the bald statement in 1962 of the US Surgeon General that 'the maximal atmospheric lead levels currently observed have been much too low to produce clinical evidence of lead poisoning.' Yet the air-lead measurements made in the US, France, Britain and elsewhere in the late 'fifties and early 'sixties were in a sense evidence of an anxiety that the situation was more dangerous than that statement suggests.

Within months of the appearance of the paper alleging chronic lead insult to the whole population, a reply appeared in the US *Archives of Environmental Health*. In this it was argued by Thomas J. Haley that the old lead-level figures were good, that to cause chronic poisoning the lead needed to be in a form that was readily absorbed and carried to target organs (which had not been demonstrated for exhaust products), that the amounts of lead absorbed via the lungs was smaller than suggested by Dr Patterson and that the notion of chronic lead insult was a myth because it would only occur at lead levels much higher than those prevailing in US cities at that time.

What was actually demonstrated in this paper was the willingness to *assume* that earlier figures were correct, and to interpret information on the absorption of lead in such a way that the hazard was minimized. True the paper showed that the build-up of blood levels requires increasingly large increments of absorbed lead as the blood-lead level rises, but it was concerned primarily with adult figures. Neither then nor now is this the section of the population that we should be most concerned about. In his statement, which incidentally resulted in the raising of the permitted levels of lead in petrol, the US Surgeon General had said that even at the levels of exposure prevalent in 1962 there were some areas of doubt about hazards, particularly those for infants, young children and individuals who for one reason or another happened to be highly sensitive. Dr Haley, on the other hand, said flatly that dangerous exposure to lead results in blood lead levels of between 0·7 ppm and 2·0 ppm (well in the adult range for industrial poisoning) and concluded that, in spite of an overall increase of 250% in the use of leaded petrol, body burdens of lead have not increased since *the main source is food, not the atmosphere*.

BOGUS THRESHOLDS

That needs looking at very hard but, for the moment, it is worth weighing a statement that occurs almost as an aside in the Haley paper. In discussing the forms in which lead poisoning can occur he gave a final mention to 'the lead encephalopathy *frequently seen in infants and children*.'[6] [My italics]

First, this kind of inflammation of the brain in infants and children is an extremely serious illness which leaves one quarter of those affected with permanent brain damage. All children who suffer lead encephalitis twice are left with permanent brain damage. Second, if the condition is 'frequently seen' then it must represent the easily visible tip of a kind of pyramid of lead intoxication that spreads through the infant and child population. In that case any reduction of the general level of lead intake must be regarded as a good thing even though it might be argued that only a small proportion are thus given protection, and it is improper if not wholly irresponsible to draw a veil over the need for this additional public security by referring only to adult blood-lead levels and adult average sensitivity.

It has turned out that, in fact, a large part of the increasingly angry discussion about the effects of leaded petrol has revolved about the interpretation of the significance of blood-lead levels in adults. Long ago the doyen of lead toxicologists, Dr R. A. Kehoe, whose studies have largely been supported by the lead industry, came through very carefully documented work to the conclusion that the onset of adult lead poisoning occurred at a blood-lead level of 0·8 ppm. This has been seized upon and quoted very frequently by those defending the present concentrations of lead in air as harmless, for adult blood-lead levels in those not industrially exposed to the metal range from around 0·16 to 0·45 ppm.

But in his own work Dr Kehoe qualifies his own recommended threshold level. Because of analytical inaccuracies, he says, it is best to take the level of 0·7 ppm. Elsewhere he says that although this can be regarded as the toxic threshold 'toxic bouts can occur with decreasing frequency down to the normal level of 0·3 ppm.' In other words, 0·7 is not a threshold at all, it is an average point of demarcation between certainty and uncertainty, with the area of uncertainty populated by all those who are more sensitive than the average. If the range of sensitivity is distributed normally around the average, that means that *half the adult population and all the infant and children would suffer toxic effects of lead at blood levels below that recommended as a threshold.*[31]

One of the weaknesses of the acceptance of blood-lead levels as a guide to the extent of lead intoxication is that it is notoriously unreliable, not because of simple variations in sensitivity between individuals, but because there appear to be major differences in the way lead can be handled by the body. In 1949, for instance, the British industrial toxicologist, R. E. Lane,[7] said that attempts to establish critical values above which poisoning occurs and below which safety may be presumed must necessarily break down. This is referring not to a whole-population exposure, but to industrial workers exposed to lead and therefore under periodic medical supervision.

In the case of infants and children the situation is even more uncertain, for the growing child handles lead in a way that is quite different to that of adults. There is evidence that the infant and child brain is more readily accessible, and that great variations occur in the amount of lead that is stored in the child skeleton at any given exposure. In adults bone storage is the third stage of the defence system, and comes into use when the normal detoxification systems of the body can no longer cope.

At existing lead-levels in advanced countries, the bone storage of adults increases with age. This may be a sign that the really safe limit has already been reached; in children it may well have been exceeded. Some infants already have to store a considerable proportion of absorbed lead in their skeleton, a situation that is dangerous because, at times of high metabolism such as that occurring during a fever, the lead is mobilized and may result in lead encephalitis *even though at the outset the level of lead in the blood was well below that normally regarded as toxic.*

But, if this has been known for some time, medical authorities have in general been slow to recognize the special susceptibility of infants and children to lead poisoning, and the conclusions of some researchers that 'even modest elevations of blood-lead may be associated with biochemical abnormalities in the child brain'[8] have received little support. The controversy surrounding the steadily rising levels of lead in the environment has been continually obscured by technical interpretation which, depending on the view required, could bend one way or the other.

Yet, unfortunately, lead levels of the blood are the best available means of measuring individual exposure. The danger lies in believing that they give some kind of absolute indication of whether or not poisoning is occurring. Such a belief is as seriously misleading as are some of the older recognition points still used by medical practitioners—such as the so-called 'blue-line' on the gums resulting from severe chronic exposure—even though a multiplicity of serious psychological and other symptoms can occur without such a handy signal turning up.

DOUBLE-THINK

So it seems that two of the weapons in the armoury of those who argue that the rising concentrations of lead in the urban environment are harmless, are themselves defective. Indeed the argument that at some time in the past or that in some parts of the world (New Guinea for example) the levels of exposure to lead have been as high as they are today is irrelevant to present considerations of public health (see note 26). As Lennart Danielson has pointed out in a review of the situation in Sweden[9] such an approach is just as erroneous as using nineteenth-century levels of bacterial contamination in hospitals as a basis for present-day hygiene. The real question is whether urban lead levels are too high and whether they will continue to rise unless something is done to control lead emissions. In general, Britain and other European countries have tended slavishly to follow the recommendations of the US Surgeon General throughout the development and growth of the widespread use of lead in petrol, although in Britain the situation has twice been reviewed by a select committee whose views, in the end, have been permissive. Doubts began to appear, however, in the late 'fifties when an American committee jointly representing the petroleum industry and the US Department of Public Health weighed up the consequences of permitting an increase in the maximum amount of lead allowed in petrol from 3 millilitres to 4 millilitres per US gallon. (This amounts to something like 6 grams per gallon, for tetra-ethyl lead is heavy.)

While concluding that the available information did not indicate that the increase would add significantly to public health hazards, the committee also noted, in a curious sentence which reveals a considerable amount of double-think, that 'a conclusive answer is impossible at the present time because of a lack of medical data.' How any committee can decide that something is without hazard if it lacks the necessary data is a question which no one seems to have asked at the time but, with the eventual concurrence of the US Surgeon General, the amount of lead in petrol was gradually raised by petrol companies to meet the growing demand for 'high performance' that was, and still is being, engendered by motor company advertising throughout the Western world.

Again, in 1965 in the US, in a report on the quality of the environment by the President's Science Advisory Committee, there is evidence of similar double-vision. It was said, among other things, that while present levels of lead were *apparently* not causing disability 'the margin of safety between present lead levels and deleterious levels is not certain.' It would have been almost better to say nothing but, as it happened, the controversy flared up very shortly afterwards when the scientific paper[5] alleging 'chronic lead insult' sailed into the arena and started the battle in earnest.

As in the case of mercury, in Europe it was Swedish scientists who took up the cudgels and began to carry out a careful evaluation of the situation. In Britain, at this time, measurements of the lead concentrations in air made in 1962–3 were incorporated into a scientific report by the Medical Research Council's Air Pollution Research Unit. Without going into the amount of lead that would be absorbed by individuals this concluded, on the basis of average lead concentrations in the air in Fleet Street, London, that levels 'were below those held to be safe by many authorities.'[10] On the other hand, the report gave emphasis to the potential problem posed by rising levels of carbon monoxide.

This report, coming as it did from an independent watch-dog agency of high repute, bolstered the euphoria at Government level without even going into the subject in detail, with the result that when further warning signs appeared they were largely ignored. Work at the Hospital for Sick Children in Great Ormond Street, London[11] revealed, in the course of studies of the relationship between lead exposure and mental subnormality, that blood-lead levels in children were scattered over a fairly wide range and that some were unexpectedly high even in control groups. The relationship between high blood-lead levels and subnormality is still an area of controversy, but in 1967 an entirely separate survey of 73 children in Manchester showed that they not only had an unexpected high average blood-lead level, but that almost 20% had blood-lead levels that exceeded 0·5 ppm.[12] Whatever the source of the lead resulting in these unusually high levels, the situation was disturbing. In their work involving various kinds of lead poisoning in Great Ormond Street the scientists there had concluded that a realistic safe threshold for children was a blood-lead level of 0·36 ppm. Small samples showed clearly that this was being exceeded by a significant proportion of the child population: in the Manchester study it was exceeded by almost 30% of those examined.

Instead of leading to much larger surveys and to a real investigation of the sources of lead causing the high blood levels, the authorities seem at this point to have turned a blind eye or, at best, to have let the matter rest. It had been shown by a number of investigations that, especially in soft water areas of which Manchester is one, lead piping could add significantly to the daily dose. Further, the children appeared to be healthy and their lead levels were still low when compared to the levels resulting from industrial exposures and to which the advisory experts were accustomed. The only seriously concerned evaluation appeared in a large article in *The Guardian* on June 27 1967 to which the major angry response came from the Lead Development Association and, more suavely, from the petroleum giants.

COMMITTED PERSUADERS

Characteristically, outside the scientific literature in which their support has been largely invisible, the industries involved in the controversy have maintained a steady if aloof viewpoint that the entire lead-scare is a phoney bogey. In the United States, where the lead issue boiled up most fiercely, it was overtaken by accident during the general environmental crisis caused by motor vehicles and climatic conditions in California. There, through increasingly stiff legislation controlling other exhaust constituents—carbon monoxide, oxides of nitrogen and unburned hydrocarbons—lead will be eliminated because if retained it would poison catalysts needed to remove the other constituents. Although in terms of general legislation such as the US Air Quality Act, 1967, and through abortive attempts to introduce a city 'lead tax' on vehicles, the anti-lead campaign bore no specific fruit for many years, lead-free petrol has been available for some time and has been backed roundly by Henry Ford himself. The first specific measures to reduce vehicle lead emissions, the mandatory reduction of engine compression ratios to allow the widespread use of low-octane fuel, comes into effect in 1972. The environmental improvement may not be really measurable before 1980.

In spite of slow if encouraging progress in the US, Britain entered the 'seventies still bearing the official view that, since the British Isles are well ventilated and seldom—if ever—have sufficient intensity of light to produce a Los Angeles type photo-chemical smog, there is little that needs doing about vehicle pollution. But this to lump all vehicle pollutants together and to disregard the important part played by exhaust aerosols in the general lead burdens of the urban population. Such a blanket argument is illogical, can be construed as administratively convenient and possibly devious, and is certainly not accepted either in Sweden or by the expert environmental sub-committee of the Council of Europe. Yet in Britain on December 18 1968, when the controversy about lead was expanding, the authoritative voice of the *British Medical Journal* came up with an unusual kind of statement. It was not a piece of original research nor a comment article, but an *ad hoc* assessment of lead hazards made by a group of scientists.

In effect it weighed the question of sub-clinical damage to the population through lead contamination and, using the by then traditional comparisons with largely industrial evidence, decided that there was no hazard. The signatories included representatives of the Imperial Smelting Company, Associated Octel and Vauxhall Motors. The statement asserted that in adults blood-lead levels of up to 0·8 ppm were 'acceptable' and, although the participation of interested industries in the establishment of standards of this kind is essential and can be taken as evidence of serious concern, it can never appear to be free from a commercial need to set the level high. This is not to say that the suggested standard has been manipulated, but that where matters of public health are concerned it is imprudent, as history has often shown, to let powerful industries forge too many of their own shackles.

The statement was, in any case, rather curiously framed. It said in effect that mild symptoms of lead poisoning were not symptoms of lead poisoning unless the blood-lead level was higher than 0·8 ppm. Since, over the years, the complexity of the relationship between blood levels and poisoning has resulted in very cautious interpretation by experts in several countries, it is difficult to understand how such a firm ruling can be reached. Furthermore it excludes the real worries, those of high levels in children, and the problem of wide variations in individual response, both of which had become larger during the three or four years before 1968. The statement, to say the least, seemed highly reactionary.

This could matter a great deal for, accepted uncritically by the major proportion of general practitioners, it would mean that the observation of early symptoms associated with lead would be blocked, thus leading to delays in the accumulation of evidence essential to the proper regulation of this aspect of public health, quite apart from widespread misdiagnosis. It seems a reasonable bet that this is in fact happening throughout the Western world. The motor enthusiast, for example, who washes engine parts in leaded petrol may not associate bouts of irritability, depression or psychological disturbance with the activity. And if he does not, then neither will his medico.

To be fair, both toxicologists and the petrol companies have, in the past, emphasized that leaded petrol should not be used for cleaning or other purposes outside its intended use in vehicles, but many people do not know this and some do not care, with the result that, here and there throughout the world, there are incidents resulting in mental disability or death. That these occur is a certain indication that lower levels of lead poisoning are more widespread although they are seldom recognized.

Looking back, then, we have a situation in which interpretation of the standard method of measurement of lead poisoning, blood-lead level, is not wholly reliable especially in children and sensitive individuals; in which arguments about whether or not higher or lower lead exposures than today occurred in earlier times are quite irrelevant to the discussion; in which, quite erroneously, advisory authorities and Governments calculate whole-population exposures on the basis of averages and on a comparison with industrial exposures, and in which early symptoms are unlikely to be observed. Let's get closer to the third point, and to the facts of the presently increasing public lead exposure. The Swedes, pushed into the serious consideration of heavy metal contamination by their mercury problem, have analysed the situation thoroughly.[13] In their Natural Science Research Council report of 1970 they cite food and air as the main sources of lead for the population. When the amount of lead in food is weighed, it is necessary to take into account a variety of contributory sources, such as the lead in soils, the use of agricultural chemicals containing lead, the possibility of contamination from lead glazes on pottery, lead solder in cans, and lead in domestic water from piping, and from fallout of the lead from vehicle exhausts. The proportionate contributions from these separate sources are very difficult to calculate because of their uneven distribution, but it is important to remember that one of the components, which turns up in rain—and therefore in water and soil—as well as in surface contamination of foods, is lead from vehicles.

Atmospheric lead, on the other hand, presents a comparatively simple picture. In Sweden the contribution from coal burning is negligible, but in the US where considerable amounts of coal are burned, analyses still show that the dominant lead component in city air comes from motor vehicles.[14] The technique used, that of comparing the ratio of lead isotopes in the compounds added to petrol, with those found in the air, would reveal any significant contribution from another source. This technique has since been used to examine airborne lead in several major cities of the world, including Paris and Amsterdam (and dust in London), with similar results.

FROM AIR TO YOU

Excluding the possibility of a significant contribution from coal in some special areas, such as the Ruhr or the midlands and northeast of England, the general situation is one in which it can safely be said that any lead found in city air will have come, predominantly, from motor vehicles exhausts. The question then becomes one of finding out what the air levels are, what the trends will be, how much of this lead is actually absorbed by individuals, and whether it forms an important part of the total absorption.

In this kind of calculation it is very important to arrive at a realistic assessment of the *maximum* possible daily intake from all sources, plus a breakdown of the component sources, and relate this to the *most vulnerable* members of the population. Average values not only reduce the apparent danger but omit the important targets. It is deceptive to take, for example, an average rate of absorption via the human lung or the human gut. To cover the whole population you must use the highest authentic values that have been found because (and this was confirmed in 1971 in a precise way through experiments at Harwell) there are very wide variations of absorption rate between individuals in otherwise identical circumstances. But, before looking at the calculations, we need to know how much lead is there, and how much will be there in, say, 1980, if present trends continue.

Now tetra-ethyl lead and tetra-methyl lead are such highly poisonous compounds that you cannot buy them. They are not included in standard chemical catalogues and are not even easily available for use in university research. Yet, in the petrol of motor vehicles, several thousand tons are dispersed each year in Britain alone. The manufacturers, Associated Octel in Britain and the US, do not and never have released information on production and sales. To get at a reasonable estimate it is necessary to work backwards from total petrol sales, the proportions of the various grades, the changing pattern of sales over the years and the amount of leading normally associated with those grades during the same period. There are a lot of unknowns in this but FIG. 3:4 is probably close to the truth for Britain, and that means 10,000 tons in 1970, 17,000 tons by 1976 and probably well over 20,000 tons by 1980. (The figures for the US are, respectively, 250,000 tons, 350,000 tons and 450,000 tons by 1980.)

Not all of that is lead but, making allowance for the organic parts of the molecule and for the lead 'lost' during burning in the engine (30% is said to be 'lost' in the engine, which amounts to about 5 lb of lead in 30,000 miles: unless it comes out of the sump with used oil and still finds its way into the environment, where does it go?) this leaves about 7000 tons of lead reaching the atmosphere in Britain now, and close to 14,000 tons by 1980. It is worth remembering that, for every mile travelled, the average saloon car pumps out 50 milligrams of lead. You can excrete only half a milligram of lead a day and, even with intakes well below that level, lead is slowly built up in tissue and bone. Further, although most of the lead alkyls in fuel are converted into inorganic compounds during combustion, a proportion of the lead coming out of a tailpipe is still in its alkyl form, an even more insidious and deadly poison than any of the inorganic forms. As in the case of organic mercury, the reason is that organic lead has a longer half-life and selectively damages

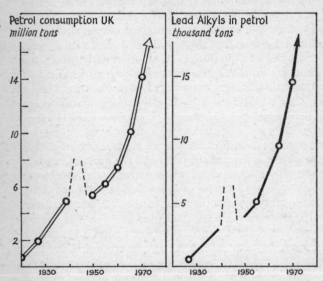

FIG. 3:4. Soaring petrol consumption in the UK and the rise in the consumption of lead alkyl 'anti-knock' agents. Because of their increasing proportional use, the rise of the lead alkyl curve is slightly faster than that of petrol.

the brain and central nervous system. Unlike mercury, however, the action is not direct but is through toxic breakdown-products produced in the liver during the processes nature designed for our protection. The body itself turns tetra-alkyl lead into a deadly brain poison.

Excluding for the moment this highly dangerous alkyl lead component of exhaust fumes (and every 'official' assessment of the urban lead contamination situation contrives to do just that), it is now clear that to arrive at the most prudent evaluation of the absorption of lead by the population you need some important measurements: the maximum air concentrations of lead likely to be met by individuals, plus the maximum acceptable absorption rate: the maximum lead concentrations likely to be met in food and, again, the maximum absorption rate.

One of the most important keys is the absorption rate and it is a curious fact that, as the concentrations of lead in urban air have risen, the absorption rates emanating from experimental work by scientists close to the lead alkyl industry have steadily declined. Until the early 'fifties the estimates made by workers in the US, centred perhaps on that of Dr R. A. Kehoe, ranged from 30% to 60% of the lead in air reaching the lungs. By the mid 'sixties, however, tentative estimates had dropped to 25% and, in 1969 both Dr Kehoe and Dr Gordon Stopps (formerly of Associated Octel) came up respectively with low figures of 10% (absorbed by the lung) and of between 20% and 30%. Outside the area of research supported by the lead industry the figures have been very different and cover the range of 30% to 90% depending on the particle size involved. Particle size is in many ways crucial for, in conjunction with the topography of the lung surface and the pattern and velocity of inhaled air, it determines what proportion of particles are deposited, and where.

So, in a sense, you can pay your money and take your choice, but before doing so it needs to be remembered that all these figures are attempts to reach an *average* value. Inevitably when industry does its sums it opts for the lower values, but it would be expected that when any protective agency did its sums it would opt for the higher figures just to be on the safe side. You might also have expected, in a situation as confused and controversial as this, that the protective agencies would initiate research aimed at resolving doubts, by arriving at unequivocal maxima for both adults and children.

COOKING THE BOOKS

In fact the protective agencies, at least in Britain, have done neither. But in Sweden, where heavy metal contamination is regarded more seriously and where legislation to reduce the amount of lead in petrol is already in operation, the survey made in 1969 and which weighed all the available evidence opted in the end to take 50% as the absorption rate for airborne lead. In sharp contrast, one of the few 'official' estimates to reach the public in detail in Britain, that of an internal memorandum of January 1970 from the Medical Research Council's Air Pollution Unit (under Professor Lawther in London) to the Department of the Environment, takes 30% as an average value while giving the impression that this is being set deliberately high as a matter of caution. There is little doubt that this report minimized the hazard and it happens that, at the time it was being prepared (on unadjusted information about street concentrations of lead that had been gathered by the unit 9 years earlier, see note 29), scientists at Harwell were arriving at some new figures for lung absorption of lead aerosols.

The right hand, it would seem, did not know what the left hand was doing and in any case was involved in special pleading. The Harwell investigation, using a radioactive lead isotope aerosol with a constant spectrum of particle size, discovered that, in a small group of volunteer human guinea pigs, the absorption rate of the lungs in identical circumstances varied from 34% up to 64%. The point about this is not simply the high upper level of absorption, but the very large variation between individuals. In parallel studies Harwell showed that the absorption rate from the gut varied between 5% and 17%. (At the time of writing these experiments are not complete and have not yet been published, although the results are known to specialists in the field.)

So it seems that the Swedish survey was right to take a high figure, but that to be really safe an even better figure would be 60%, double that taken by the Medical Research Council in Britain. Further, that in calculating the absorption from food the normally accepted figure of between 5% and 10% should really be upgraded to 15%. These adjustments, when applied to present and predicted lead levels, result in disturbing conclusions.

One of the unfortunate aspects of any calculations about lead contamination is that nowhere in the world, not even in the US where serious measurements have been made for many conditions of traffic in many cities, have sufficient measurements been made for reliable assessments to be made about the variation of exposure likely to occur during a normal day's movements from home, to office or school or shops, in vehicles of various kinds, and during the night. There are great uncertainties and, although the purpose of environmental research is to reduce uncertainties so that better assessments can be made, far too little has been done in this field. It is rumoured that, some years ago, the lead alkyl and motor industries in the US carried out a survey of the air-lead levels in vehicles of various ages, but that the results were so disturbing that they were never published. But, rumour apart, it takes little imagination to realize that in heavy traffic and with air intakes close to exhaust level the build up of lead levels in a closed car could be considerable even without the direct exhaust leakages likely in older vehicles.

The only firm information available comprises the best measurements made in cities throughout the world during the past ten years, plus the predictions implicit in the rising consumption of leaded petrol. It is important to remember that many of us live beside busy urban or city streets, that many children play on city streets that are rich in lead dust from vehicles and paint (6000 ppm was recorded in London some years ago, and the figures were higher for Zurich, see FIG. 3:5), spend many hours of the day in city schools or, perhaps worse, in parked prams close to traffic in shopping areas, and that when lead levels are highest, during the day, then the rate of inhalation is also highest.

All this confirms that to be prudent the interpretation of exposures should be liberal and that to get an assessment of, say, the daytime background levels common in city schools, it is no use applying values obtained by taking measurements at some other site 50 or 150 feet above the

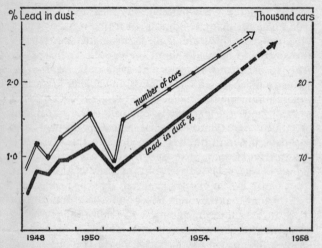

FIG. 3:5. Relationship between number of vehicles and the lead concentration of dust in the city of Zurich. By 1962 the lead concentration of London street dust was in some areas about 6%. The figures for all major cities are similar. (After Lennart Danielson.)

ground as has been the demonstrable practice in Britain and the US. You need measurements at nose level.

Working from all the available information, which shows city lead levels in streets to range from 3·0 micrograms per cubic metre to 71·3 micrograms per cubic metre (Hollywood freeway[15]), the Swedish survey concluded that, by taking 5 micrograms/m³ as a reasonable daytime level for Stockholm in conjunction with an urban night time level of 2 micrograms/m³, a prudent daily mean level would be 3 micrograms/m³. On the British measurements of 1962–3 that showed a Fleet Street mean of 3·2 micrograms/m³ this looks high, but traffic and lead emission doubled between 1962 and 1969 so that, for large British cities—and indeed cities throughout the Western world—the Swedish estimate, even though full of uncertainties, may sensibly cover the top range of individual exposures.

Before looking at what this means in terms of lead inside your body, take a brief look again at the rate of growth of lead emissions predicted from present trends in petrol consumption (FIG. 3:4). They are expected, in European and other advanced cities, to double by 1976 and double again by the early 'eighties. This *must* mean that lead levels will become higher, that areas of high lead level will become larger, and the downward gradients when moving away from busy streets will become less steep. It is a reasonable assumption that, as emissions double, so will human absorption, and so will the proportion of lead in city dust. And it needs to be remembered that city dust does not simply lie about the streets. It blows on to the food in shops, on to the ice-creams of children, adheres to sticky fingers and gets licked off, gets on to the lettuce in urban gardens and into urban soils, gets circulated in its finest particles with the air mass to be rained out elsewhere and add to the general lead burdens of food and soil to form a real if incalculable part of the general lead burden.

This kind of secondary distribution, which necessarily transfers part of the initially airborne lead burden into the food cycle is ignored in most official assessments, partly perhaps because it cannot be accurately measured. Yet it is a factor that should not be ignored. So, the interpretation of the lead problem is fraught with uncertainties which, collectively, can result in conclusions that are widely different. How much air, for example, does a man breathe each day, and does he breathe significantly less air during the night when he is away from the areas of extreme lead contamination? An active child at, say, eight years of age, who plays with typical non-stop vigour in city streets, breathes more air than an active adult. But how much more, and are the absorption rates of the younger and more efficient child lung higher, on average, than those of adults? To remove some of the uncertainties these questions need precise answers which are not, perhaps will not be, available in time.

Some workers in industrial hygiene take the average adult figure to be 15 cubic metres of air a day while others assume the higher figure of 20 cubic metres a day. Some workers, in calculating the daily intake of lead from vehicles, assume that there is a considerable 'background' level of airborne lead from other sources, and therefore deduct this from their calculated totals, while others simply separate the totals of absorption from food and air without acknowledging the contribution that airborne lead makes to the lead from food. A complicated and difficult situation to interpret and one which propagandists and politicians can exploit to their own ends and to the danger of the public.

By taking virtually every assumption that would minimize the calculated intake of lead from the atmosphere for instance, and the word *assumption* needs to be stressed, Britain's Medical Research Council Air Pollution Unit arrived at the reassuring conclusion that even for individuals working in the busiest streets for eight hours a day the elimination of lead from petrol would reduce their daily lead absorption by only 7%. Within weeks of the first announcement of this result in January 1971, it had been quoted twice by the Government spokesman in the House of Lords, three times by the Minister of the Environment, Mr Peter Walker, and frequently by petroleum spokesmen.

DELAYED DECISIONS

Now it is well known that, when faced with the prospect of a difficult and unpopular decision, individuals and Governments alike will grasp at any apparently authentic evidence that will either delay the need for decision or demonstrate that the decision is not even necessary. This, quite apart from the bad science that results from unsupported assumptions, is one of the most important reasons for extreme responsibility on the part of public watch-dog agencies. Even with the growth of a healthy public scepticism, if the independent Medical Research Council (MRC) says that things are OK then the man in the street is likely to accept this opinion as unprejudiced and reliable. He certainly does not look for bias in the underlying *assumptions* or, and this is perhaps even more important, for bias in the assumptions which helps to confirm a view of the situation that has been expressed at some time in the past by the same scientific group and which is largely an expression of commitment.

In looking at the MRC's conclusion that, at most, 7% of your daily dose of lead comes from vehicles it is important to remember, not that others have reached very different conclusions, but that in 1965 when the lead controversy was just beginning to become a public issue in Britain and in the rest of Europe, the MRC published the conclusion that concentrations of lead in the air 'were below those held to be safe by many authorities.'[16] If somewhat obliquely, the commitment was to a view which minimized the potential hazard.

So, since public health is involved, let's take the other and more appropriate view that we need to know the maximum potential contributions from vehicle exhausts to the lead hazard. Since all the available evidence suggests that the dominant source of airborne lead is the motor vehicle, it is inadmissible to pretend that there is some other important 'background' source, unless this can be shown to exist. And, since there is a wide variation between individuals of absorption rate, we should take the highest appropriate absorption levels, not some arbitrary average.

Taking the Swedish figure of 3 micrograms of lead per cubic metre in city and urban air, a respiration rate of 20 cubic metres a day and a 60% absorption rate (which is slightly lower than the peak suggested as possible by Harwell, although the Harwell figure is not based on an aerosol of the same structure as exhaust particles), the daily dose of lead turns out to be 36 micrograms from the air. But 2% to 10% of this is organic lead, which is at least twice as dangerous as inorganic lead. So we need to add a danger factor of, say, 6%, which comes out close to 2 micrograms a day and takes the total to 38 micrograms daily.

Curiously, while there are great differences of opinion on air absorption, almost all authorities agree that the daily intake of lead from food is about 300 micrograms. Again, taking the highest appropriate absorption figure for the gut, 15%, this gives a daily absorption of 45 micrograms a day. But a proportion of this comes from the lead in the air, so there needs to be an adjustment. No one, however, knows what that adjustment should be. What can be said is that, if the dominant source of airborne lead is from motor vehicles then it might fall in the range of 5% to 15%. In such an uncertain situation and, *since it will not affect the outcome of the calculation seriously*, an average figure is probably acceptable. This means that the daily absorption from food goes down to 40·5 micrograms, while that from air goes up to 42·5 micrograms. In short, more than half (52%) of your daily dose of lead comes from the air.

Which is right, 7% or 52%? Probably neither, for the calculations in both cases employ unsupported assumptions. Yet, with the prudence that should mediate decisions affecting public health, it is wisest to lean towards the higher rather than the lower figure. This means that it would be irresponsible for either Government or industry to use the lower figure as a basis for policy decisions. One depressing fact about the British MRC calculation was that it blandly claimed that an air absorption rate of 30% was 'extreme'. This was true in relation only to industrial estimates, not to estimates made by scientists outside industry.

With so much uncertainty about, and the possibility of bias in every assessment of the situation, what is the proper course? One way of resolving things would be for Governments to initiate essential research in independent agencies aimed at narrowing the uncertainties and determining the hazard to the most sensitive members of the public. That is fine when there are several years of apparent safety in hand. But as urban blood-lead levels are already overlapping those at which clinically accepted poisoning occurs, and since recent work has shown that lead interferes with the enzymes concerned with red-cell synthesis,[17] (see also note 8) at levels well below those common today, it is much too late to wait for the results of new research.

The only practical questions are whether lead burdens are too high (which they certainly are), which are the major and growing sources (and the answer must include lead in petrol for it is the fastest growing significant source), and which sources can most easily be controlled? Again, the answer must include lead in petrol, for it is neither necessary for the production of high octane fuels, nor essential for any other engineering reason. The scare of greatly increased costs associated with leadless petrol, launched by the oil companies in the late 60s, was soon seen to be a red herring. There would, it is true, be major refinery modifications to pay for at a cost to the consumer of about US 2 cents (UK $\frac{1}{2}$p) a gallon. But the US giant Standard Oil performed a neat about-face in 1971 by publicly declaring that the increased cost of petrol would be more than compensated by reduced maintenance costs and longer engine life. Gulf Oil followed this by announcing a technique that would actually reduce production costs. The motorist has nothing to lose, and the public has everything to gain.

LEAD RED-HERRINGS

But what about the other sources? In the British MRC's memorandum of January 1971 the proposition that the burning of coal provided a significant 'background' level of airborne lead was raised for the first time and, although the memorandum was sharply criticized in the British press as being 'dangerously simplistic', the coal question has not been resolved. Clearly, if coal is a major source then, in Britain and West Germany at least, something should be done about it.

Coal was thrown into the lead debate at a time very convenient, politically and scientifically, for those wishing to minimize the problem posed by vehicles. This is typical of the pattern of environmental battles. Although peripheral it serves to take attention away from the main issue while also diminishing its importance. Unfortunately the lead in coal question cannot be answered precisely. Since lead is not very valuable no one has taken a serious look at the possibility of its extraction from coal or coke. Measurement, made in the UK, the US and Germany suggest that inorganic lead is present in concentrations which vary widely between coal types and locations, and may be anything from 8 ppm to 800 ppm or more. Britain's National Coal Board, without a full spectrum of measurements, suggests that 20 ppm is a good average figure for the UK. That of West Germany is higher. But for both the UK and the US an average figure of 50 ppm should cover all possible errors, although in this context too averages can be dangerous because they overlook high local contamination.

At first glance even the average looks serious from the point of view of general contamination. Britain and the US burn 120 million tons and 550 million tons of coal a year respectively, so the simplistic view is that 6000 tons and 27,500 tons of lead a year reach their atmospheres, almost as much (in the UK at least) as comes from vehicles. But a high proportion of lead is retained in ash, much of the lead which volatilizes condenses out again in flues and stacks, and in both Britain and the US a large proportion of the coal is in any case burned in power stations (80 million tons in the UK) where through the use of electrostatic precipitators over 95% of the particulate matter is extracted. True, comparing lead with the volatilization curves of those rarer metals which have been examined, such as germanium, it looks as though there could be some escape of volatilized lead from domestic grates. But even allowing for the unlikely escape of 10% of coal-lead as vapour, this amounts to only 200 tons for the 40 million tons of coal burned in British homes each year. The amount of coal burned directly in the US is negligible. The overall US picture, however, is less certain.

In Britain the other 80 million tons of coal are burned predominantly in power stations, where the stack precipitators vary in efficiency but retain between 95% and 99% of the particles that might reach the atmosphere. At most something like 3% of the lead might escape which, on 80 million tons, comes to 120 tons a year. So it looks as though the total atmospheric contamination from coal in Britain amounts to less than 320 tons (about 900 tons in the US), and that these figures are probably far too high because they are based on extreme assumptions all the way. Compared to the 10,000 tons coming from petrol in the UK (250,000 tons US), the amounts are almost insignificant. Britain's National Coal Board, when challenged in 1971, actually claimed that at the outside 200 tons reached the atmosphere from coal each year but, because of the incomplete information on which their calculation is based, the result needs to be accepted with reservations.[18]

Yet this kind of coarse calculation, which certainly cannot be wrong to more than plus or minus 50%, is easy to carry out, and its basic information is readily available. There are areas of doubt and until lead is looked at seriously as a contaminant by all the authorities involved, it will remain a 'guesstimate.' But why, if available information indicated that coal was *not* a significant contributor to airborne lead contamination, did the MRC and (later) the petrol industry, introduce coal into the lead discussion? They had not done the simple sums but, instead, blindly asserted that it provided a significant background level of contamination. Even if well meant its introduction can be construed as a deliberate red-herring designed to divert attention from the main problem.

LEAD ON TAP

There are, it is true, considerable gaps in the coal contamination story, but these are by no means as large as those in knowledge of the contribution of *water* to the daily dose of lead. Back in 1963 the World Health Organization, which serves as the international regulator of food and water standards, recommended that water *from the tap* should contain no more than 50 micrograms of lead per litre (0·05 ppm). Such a very low level makes sense because most of us consume the best part of 2 litres of water a day (and some drink a lot more) while, in cooking, water contaminants which do not vaporize at low temperatures become increasingly concentrated as the water evaporates. You may start cooking a green vegetable with water containing 0·05 ppm and end up with water containing 0·25 ppm, and this will comprise the 70% or so of water in the vegetable material! So this can make a very significant contribution of poison to the diet.

But in Europe and the United States alike, local water authorities are rarely capable of carrying out on a protectively significant basis the refined analyses required to determine contaminants at the low levels set by the WHO and, in the case of small authorities which dominate in parts of England and in Europe, are unlikely on the basis of present charges for public water ever to be able to afford the staff and equipment needed for such detailed monitoring. So there is a treble problem. Water authorities do not in general maintain WHO standards because they are not capable of doing so: unless the organizational structure changes and water costs rise they will not be able to do so in the near future, and even when water entering the mains is up to WHO standards, no one has any idea what its standards are by the time it comes out of your tap.

Official calculations of the amount of lead (or of any other contaminant) in the diet do not always include contributions from water or water-based drinks but, even assuming that WHO standards are maintained, a normal intake of fluids could contribute an additional 100 micrograms of lead a day. In areas served by reservoirs that are in or close to urban concentrations, or have major motor roads passing close to them, a significant proportion of the lead in the water could come from the fallout of airborne material. This cross-over of lead from one part of the environment to another again weakens the argument that, because the daily absorption of lead from food and water may be as large as that from the air, then the effect of reducing airborne lead would be small. The reduction could, in fact, be very much larger than is at present believed.

Yet in urban water supplies it is already clear that one of the major sources of high levels of contamination at the tap is lead piping, particularly in soft water areas where the pipes do not become accidentally lined with a protective coating of calcium. Most property built before 1939 and some since then makes use of internal lead piping and a random survey of domestic tap water in British towns carried out in 1969–70 by J. A. Tolley and C. D. Reed at the department of civil engineering at Liverpool University, found that in 9 out of 40 towns water taken directly from the tap at various times of the day exceeded the 1963 WHO permitted level of lead.[19] Similar findings were made at about the same time in West Germany and in the United States. To the bewilderment of those becoming increasingly concerned about the impact of lead contamination on public health, one of the results of these findings was that, in 1970, the World Health Organization *doubled* the permitted lead level in tap water. Even accepting this illogical step, the Liverpool University findings remain important, for three of the towns surveyed, Motherwell, Newcastle-upon-Tyne and Gateshead, provided water samples whose lead content exceeded the new and relaxed WHO standard.

MANIPULATED STANDARDS

But why did the WHO so precipitantly decide to slacken its standards for tap water? The argument that, in general, the lead contamination situation was improving certainly could not apply. Nor indeed could the argument be applied that individual drinking water consumption in Europe is low, unless the expert committee falsely isolated water from other sources of lead. Since the technical arguments for more stringent precautions have become steadily stronger during the past decade it might be thought that either these were presented in a partial or corrupt way, or that some other pressure for a reduction of standards was overwhelming. (See note 30.)

How can member Governments maintain WHO standards if these are set at levels unattainable by the various national systems of monitoring and control? In a situation where a national protective agency takes the view of an expert advisory body (such as Britain's MRC) that lead contamination is of little public danger, then the pressures of politics, economics and convenience will have an ally in the active promotion of imprudence. The result will not only be a delay in the application of higher standards but also frustration of attempts to establish adequate monitoring and control procedures. These can easily be seen as an unwanted and unnecessary expense but, tacitly, they also demonstrate that past advisors and established practices are wrong. Elusive and internal pressures of this kind would, in an ideal world, be more notional than real, but the truth is that Governments as well as the public have to beware of committed vipers in their midst. No authority likes to be challenged, particularly on grounds which involve technicalities or analytical techniques which are beyond its grasp. The usual response is obstruction, either with the intention of doing nothing or to create a breathing space for the development of know-how needed for defence. Water authorities, throughout the Western world, have been forced on to the defensive and although some Governments are now beginning to stimulate change, the situation in 1971 was that few authorities in Europe or the United States were in a position to make essential measurements of contaminants.

It can be seen that, in all this, the main considerations can all too easily become economics, politics, convenience, obstruction, scientific commitment and the introduction of misleading interpretations of the situation. That people may be getting far too much lead appears to be of secondary importance. The Liverpool University group, for example, claim to have met continuous obstruction from water authorities and, although their results have been regularly transmitted to the relevant Government Departments (Housing and Local Government, Health and more recently, the Department of the Environment) there has been no apparent response. It is almost as though internal Government advisory pressure is deliberately blocking the acceptance of important environmental information so that, from the outside, there seems to be a conspiracy of silence.

In Britain this may change dramatically as the Government's central scientific advisory unit (a kind of Department of the Environment 'think-tank' attached to the power machine of the Cabinet Office) gets fully into its stride, for there are already signs that prevailing 'official' views are being sharply scrutinized. What the change really means is that the scientific and technical arguments will be first weighed outside the context in which, at the present time, they are subject to all manner of industrial and political pressures. Further, that in interpreting the value of evidence both its source and the commitment of its originators will receive proper weighting.

But there are extremely subtle pressures also at work which are not only difficult to interpret but virtually impossible to unmask. Take, for instance, the *British Medical Journal* statement on blood-lead levels in December 1968. Although this was presented as of general relevance to the problem of whole-population blood-lead levels, and treated as such in an accompanying leading article, the academic signatories—who included Prof. A. Goldberg at Glasgow—regarded this as a statement on *industrial exposure.* How it came to be presented in the medical press in such a way that the medical profession would regard it as generally applicable may never be discovered, but it will have misled the nation's GPs.

It happens that, in spite of obstruction, much larger and more detailed water surveys are now underway both at Liverpool University and, under Prof. Goldberg, at Glasgow University, which might eventually provide enough information for a statistically reliable interpretation of water contamination in Britain. Even without the results of these surveys one serious new hazard is already apparent. Authorities in general believe that since lead piping is going out of use and being replaced, at least on the cold water side, by plastic, the lead problem is declining. But the PVC being used for water pipes *includes a filler containing lead which, when new, results in higher lead contamination of water than lead piping itself*, and when matured results in lead contamination whose levels are similar to those normally encountered with the older kind of piping. It seems incredible that such a crazy situation can have been allowed to develop, but it reveals in a pointed way the gross inefficiency of the structures supposed to protect public health.

OLD AND NEW EVIDENCE

But what evidence is there that public health is likely to be affected by lead in quantities so small that they are measured in millionths of a gram? First, those scientific investigators who have been concerned either with lead in children or with the effects of lead on human biochemistry have consistently recommended the lowering of the blood-lead levels above which damaging effects must be presumed to occur. The group at the London Hospital for Sick Children suggested 0·36 ppm for children; in California the public health authorities have suggested 0·5 for adults and, in 1971, Prof. A. Goldberg suggested 0·3 for children and 0·4 for adults. All these recommended safe levels are commonly exceeded in children and adults in the general population. There is even justification, through experimental evidence and observed effects on people, for believing that these newly recommended levels will in the long-term have to be again revised downward.

Working experimentally with rats, Prof. H. A. Schroeder of Dartmouth College Medical School, New Hampshire, who is perhaps the world's leading authority on the effects of trace elements on man, discovered long ago that the addition of 5 ppm of lead to an otherwise lead-free diet resulted not only in a higher incidence of disease and of mortality during the first three months of life, but that the average life-span was reduced by 24·2%.[20] To anyone who believes in the mass effect laws of chemistry this is a very significant and disturbing finding but, simply because of the size of the experimental sample that would be necessary to demonstrate the proportional effect expected at the dietary lead levels common to humans, it is not feasible to *prove* that folk are dying earlier than they should because of atmospheric and other lead.

And, because everyone is affected by many contaminants, a depression in life-span could not be pinned on any one of them, especially at a time when improvements in public health tend to obscure other effects on the pattern of the death rate.

But the average life-span of the American male is no longer increasing and some of the symptoms of early lead poisoning, gastric trouble, anaemia, depression, irritability and neurological and psychological disorders, are not only widespread in advanced societies but can precipitate the heart conditions that now dominate as a cause of premature death. It happens that the connecting thread between lead and these early symptoms is confirmed by some research which, carried out in Edinburgh in 1965, has never been published. Its author, a final year MD, was killed in a road accident shortly after this work—his thesis—was completed.[21] In an extremely painstaking and detailed way this work not only documents correlations between high lead levels in water with a number of symptoms, but also reveals that these symptoms were in the course of medical practice treated as normal occurrences without any attempt to seek their cause. (See also note 27.)

This kind of information, allied to the suppression of general medical alertness to the possibility of early symptoms of lead poisoning in the general public, especially in children, provides a strong general pointer that things are far from well. The situation was summarized powerfully in February 1971 by Professor Derek Bryce-Smith in the journal *Chemistry in Britain*. Pulling together recent evidence on the inhibition of blood enzyme systems by lead, and of the rising lead levels in the population, the article pointed out that accepted toxic levels were already being approached and in some cases exceeded (FIGS. 3:2 and 3:6). The vulnerability of children was given special emphasis: 'Children and young people appear to be specially liable to suffer more or less permanent brain damage, leading *inter alia* to mental retardation, irritability and bizarre behaviour patterns. Lead-induced psychosis is said to show striking similarities to the manic-depressive type.'[22] It needs to be stressed that these symptoms are quite different from those of adults. 'An unpleasant feature,' wrote Prof. Bryce-Smith, 'is that lead may be remobilized (from bone) long after the initial

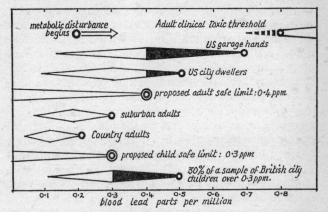

FIG 3:6. Diagrammatic representation of the present blood-lead levels of different population groups. The dark sectors indicate levels in excess of those suggested as whole population maxima by Prof. Abraham Goldberg in 1971. Interference by lead with blood enzymes occurs at well below the level shown for metabolic disturbance. Most of the data comes from the United States.

absorption, e.g. under conditions of abnormally high calcium metabolism such as feverish illness, during cortisone therapy and also in old age. It can cross the placental barrier and enter the foetus.'[23]

Predictably, within a few weeks, the petroleum industry through the Institute of Petroleum came up with a reply which, described innocently 'as a further contribution to the discussion,'[24] dismissed organic lead pollution as a negligible risk, leaned on industrial lead levels as an indication of public safety, called the Arctic evidence of global contamination into doubt and pointed out that acute lead poisoning had been steadily diminishing for years. It also emphasized the economic penalties and the considerable technical problems which would result from the removal of lead from petrol. The US plan, it said, 'is to produce, lower-compression less-economical engines which will run on unleaded or low-lead fuel, and permit the use of catalytic devices in the exhaust system—though at some overall cost to the user.'[25]

But, with the engulfing of the lead problem by the larger exhaust pollution problem in the United States, is that what is really happening? Quite apart from recent studies such as the allegedly suppressed 'Five City Study' uncovered by the environmental lobby which shows that between 1962 and 1969 the average lead levels in city air rose by more than 60%, there is evidence that, while giving the impression of backing the clean-up of lead, the petroleum giants are in fact turning the situation to profit while taking steps which actually *increase* the amount of lead reaching the atmosphere.

This effect might be accidental, but it results from the redistribution of lead stemming from the production of lead-free petrol. The higher octane hydrocarbons are being concentrated in the lead-free grade to provide a motor spirit which meets the requirements of most US engines. The resulting reduction in high octane fractions in the other grades results in the need for more lead if their octane rating is to remain unchanged. The overall result, since proportionately the leaded grades constitute the major part of the market and since their increased lead content far outweighs the lead saving represented by the leadless fuel, is a marked increase in the amount of lead coming out of the nation's tailpipes. What is more, because the price of lead-free petrol is higher than its octane-comparable leaded fuel, the pressure is necessarily towards increased lead in the environment.

This is bound to be condemned by the environmental lobby as a typical example of the extreme cynicism of big industry and, to the extent that it has been hidden, they are right. But when the pressures of an environmental cause become overwhelming before a logical solution can be formulated, then it is almost inevitable that the outcome will be bizarre, possibly dangerous, and will as far as possible be turned to profit by the industries under pressure. Environmental issues cannot be resolved by a dialogue of war: they can only be won by reasoned persuasion.

But, you might rightly ask, how much reasoned persuasion is needed to move monolithic and massive industrial enterprises and uninterested Government agencies? The case against lead in petrol seems so strong that it is extraordinary that market manipulations which result in an increased lead insult can still be allowed to happen. The onus of proof that something, known to be highly dangerous, is in fact highly dangerous to the kids in city streets, seems ultimately to rest on the conscience of a handful of independent scientists and on the perception of the public media. Scientists, because of their training, move with extreme caution for they know that, if they do otherwise, their watchful brethren will be only too pleased to move in and tear their arguments to pieces. The media are caught in the cross-fire and, to put it simply, tend to end up cross-eyed. No one wants to believe that he is being poisoned, so most do not. (See note 28.)

Yet, with the May issue of the journal of the Institute of Biology in London, came a new warning. An analysis of the British statistics on mental health revealed an unexpected and unexplained large rise in the incidence of mental illness among children (FIG. 3:7). Since children in the age groups involved, 5–8 and 9–14, are not subject to the social and other pressures associated with increases in adult mental illness, and since the proportional increase is in any case much higher in the children's groups, some new environmental factor seems to be at work. Further, it is one which appears to selectively affect children. Without claiming any causal relationship the author, again Prof. Bryce-Smith, points out that lead in the environment could be one of the factors involved, for this is precisely the kind of effect lead would produce. Do we really need to wait any longer? The truth is that, like cigarette packets, leaded-petrol pumps should carry a

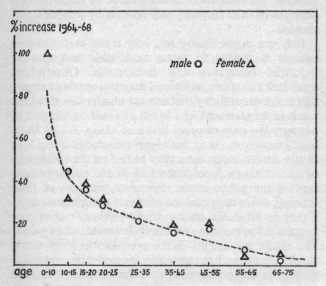

FIG. 3:7. First admissions to mental hospitals and similar units in Britain during the period 1964-8, analysed in age groups. The startling increase in first admissions in the younger groups is completely unexplained. Re-admissions over the same period were stable in all age groups. (After Prof. D. Bryce-Smith.)

warning and it should be explicit. **This substance can send you mad.**

That it can also induce other illnesses goes without saying. Some recent work carried out by the Swiss Society of Preventative Medicine is of particular interest. A group of almost 400 city residents, all of known long-term exposure to exhaust lead fumes and all suffering from ill-defined disorders, such as high fatigue, depression and digestive upsets, were treated with the chelating agent calcium EDTA (calcium di-sodium ethylene-diamine tetra-acetate). In this case the chelating agent works by exchanging its calcium for lead in the body, so that the rest of the EDTA molecule wraps round the lead, renders it mobile and allows it to be excreted. Complete cures were achieved in 65% of the cases and marked improvement occurred in a further 20%. Since this treatment also included vitamin supplements and no blood-lead analyses were carried out, the results may not be wholly unambiguous. But they are so suggestive that it would be folly to ignore them or to smear them and thereafter ignore them as has been the attitude of some industrial hygienists in Britain and the United States.

That important findings can be ignored or their implications distorted is confirmed by the frequent failure of those assessing the lead problem to refer to a series of case studies reported by two Boston (Mass.) doctors almost 30 years ago. These showed that *mild* lead poisoning in infancy or early childhood resulted, in 19 out of the 20 cases studied, in delayed behavioural and mental disturbances of a serious and permanent kind. Over the years and long after the disappearance of the initial symptoms (themselves so slight in many of the cases that they could easily have been missed) signs of new damage to the nervous system appeared. 'Under the chemical shifts common in childhood concentrations of lead known to be significant may be recurrently liberated into the circulation,' said the authors. *The presence or absence of involvement of the nervous system at the outset bore no relation to the ultimate effects.* Indeed the only child in the group not to suffer later behavioural effects— which included dyslexia, poor handwriting, pyromania, unpredictable ill-temper and the rejection of authority and schooling—had suffered the most severe initial symptoms.[32] The implications of these findings to the metal-soaked societies of the West are so important that it is almost incredible that they have never been followed up and, as far as I can discover, have been only rarely quoted but never fully discussed by those concerned with public health.

That we do not know with absolute certainty what the individual effects are on children or adults, and that it is impossible to disentangle the contribution to physical or mental disturbance of a single contaminant in a complex contamination situation, are points which miss the main issue. With unexplained trends towards increased mental disturbance in children and increased depressive illness in adults, both of which are characteristic of the effects of lead, it seems to be absolute madness to go on pumping vast quantities into the atmosphere. The adults of the US in 1971 unleashed 3 grams of lead for every child in the population, as well as 3 grams for themselves. Yet poisonous amounts of lead are measured in thousandths of a gram. To those who look back on this age society's guilt may seem as large as that of Government and industry.

EPILOGUE

(The Medical Research Council's dubious assurance on lead had been given in the House of Lords on March 10.)

A Tragi-comedy in one act: Source Hansard: vol 316: No. 76: March 24 1971.

Scene: House of Lords: the time 2.40 pm.

The Characters: Lord O'Hagan, a young and vigorous peer who takes seriously both social and environmental problems. Lord Mowbray and Stourton, Government spokesman on the environment. And others.

LORD O'HAGAN: My Lords, I beg leave to ask the Question which stands in my name on the order paper. (To ask Her Majesty's Government what they intend to do about lead in petrol.)

LORD M & S: As I told the noble Lord on March 10, HM Government are considering whether any action is needed to reduce the lead content of petrol.

LORD O'HAGAN: ... As the noble Lord is not able to speak again, may I ask him a question so that he can? Does he accept that catalysts in after-burners are poisoned by lead? And even if he is not able to accept that will he publish the evidence on which he based his earlier and rather complacent reply?

LORD M & S: ... catalysts used in America for the after-burner are poisoned by lead. May I ask the noble Lord to repeat his second question?

LORD O'HAGAN: ... will the noble Lord publish the evidence on which he based his views?

LORD M & S: ... The evidence on which I based my information was worked out by the Medical Research Council, as I informed him. I can absolutely vouch for its accuracy.

LORD O'HAGAN: ... Is the noble Lord saying that what is poisonous in America is not poisonous here?

LORD M & S: No, my Lords. What I said is that the catalyst is destroyed by any presence of lead in petrol. ...

LORD SHACKLETON: My Lords, is the noble Lord aware that I think the House is nearly as confused as he is by his answer? I wonder whether he would now take advice from the noble Lord, Lord O'Hagan, and choose an opportunity to speak again ...?

LORD AMULREE: My Lords, surely the issue is whether the amount of lead in petrol which comes out of exhaust fumes ... is likely to be deleterious to health.

LORD M & S: ... We accept that lead in itself is not a good thing to have: we are not going to give ourselves more. What we must also realize, though, is that even the natives in New Guinea have an enormous intake of lead. The amount of extra lead we get from pollution by exhaust gases is comparatively small. I accept that we would be better without it, but if we do without it we have to use a lower octane petrol . . . it is a matter of economics and sense.

LORD HENLEY: My Lords, how will this affect the lead in the noble Lord's pencil?

LORD SHACKLETON: . . . is the noble Lord aware that he has made a very serious statement. I understand that there are cannibals in New Guinea. Is he aware that there is already concern about the edibility of Western people because of the amount of DDT in them? How do DDT and lead mix? Is this not a matter for the Food and Agriculture Office?

LORD M & S: My Lords, I can assure the noble Lord the leader of the Opposition that we are not importing any cannibal meat from New Guinea.

With this, their noble Lordships turned their attentions to another matter, that of religious broadcasting.

Notes and References

1. J. J. Chisholm: 'Lead Poisoning,' *Scientific American*, February 1971.

2. C. C. Patterson: presentation to the subcommittee on air and water pollution of the US Senate Committee on Public Works, June 15 1966.

3. H. A. Schroeder and others: 'US Journal of Chronic Diseases,' pp 408–25, 1961.

4. J. D. Salvia and C. C. Patterson: 'Scientist and Citizen' (now 'Environment') April 1968.

5. C. C. Patterson: 'Natural and Contaminated Environments of Man,' *Archives of Environmental Health*, vol 11:344–60, 1965.

6. T. J. Haley: 'Chronic lead intoxication from environmental contamination: Myth or Fact?' *Archives of Environmental Health*, vol 12:781–5, 1966.

7. R. E. Lane: *British Journal of Industrial Medicine:* vol 6:125, 1949.

8. J. A. Miller and others: *Lancet*, October 3 1970, p 625.

9. L. Danielson: 'Gasoline Containing Lead,' Swedish Natural Science Research Council, Ecological Research Committee Bulletin No 6, January 1970.

10. R. E. Waller and others: 'Air pollution of a city street,' *British Journal of Industrial Medicine*, vol 22:128, 1965.

11. A. A. Moncrieff and others: *British Medical Journal*: vol 3:174, 1967.

12. N. Gordon and others: *British Medical Journal*: vol 2:480, 1967.

13. Danielson: see reference 9.

14. J. F. Chow and M. S. Johnson: 'Lead isotopes in gasoline aerosols of the Los Angeles basin,' *Science*: vol 147:502–3, 1965.

15. V. J. Konoponsky and J. B. Upham: 'Commuter exposure to atmospheric lead': *Archives of Environmental Health*: vol 14: 589–93, 1967.

16. Waller: see reference 10.

17. S. Hernberg and J. Nikkanen: *Lancet*, June 10 1970, p 63.

18. Considerable amounts of heavy metals will nevertheless reach the *environment* in ash and flue-dust, and from industrial plants such as coking ovens during recharging. (For example, see report of cattle poisoning in British Coal Utilisation Research Assn. Monthly Bulletin: No 12: vol 26:401–30, 1962.) Domestic coal fires may make some contribution to atmospheric lead in some parts of Britain, but the continuing extension of smokeless zones under the Clean Air Acts will steadily improve the situation. A recent isotopic analysis of the lead in London dust (J. F. Chow—not yet published) indicates that the predominant source is lead from motor vehicles.

19. J. A. Tolley and C. D. Reed: 'Toxic Substances in drinking water,' *Zeitschrift Vitalstoffe-Zivilisationskrankheiten*, No 6, 1968.

20. H. A. Schroeder and others: 'Chromium, Cadmium and Lead in rats: effects on life span, tumours and tissue levels,' *US Journal of Nutrition*, vol 86:51–66, May 1965.

21. A. T. Wilson: 'Lead Absorption and the Health of a Community', MD thesis, University of Edinburgh Medical School, 1965 (unpublished).

22. D. Bryce-Smith: 'Lead pollution — a growing hazard to public health,' *Chemistry in Britain*, vol 7:254–6, February 1971.

23. ibid.

24. A. L. Mills: 'Lead in the Environment,' *Chemistry in Britain*: vol 7:4:160–2, April 1971.

25. See reference 24.

26. In arguments attempting to demonstrate the harmlessness of present lead levels the evidence of ancient, medieval and modern skeletal lead-levels is often used to 'prove' that the situation now is no worse than in the past. Quite apart from the uncertainties arising from the question of whether old and undocumented samples can be taken as representative, the ancient practices of metal technology and such things as the use of lead in wine completely confuse the issue and make such comparisons worthless. It is no less pointless to introduce, as is frequently the case in Britain, the evidence of populations with a high natural exposure to lead. In Britain lead apologists often point out that the natives of New Guinea have blood levels similar to those in advanced technological societies. The native of New Guinea are not notable either for intellectual achievement or for reliable public health data.

27. Reporting a 6-year survey of lead workers carried out by the medical branch of the British Factory Inspectorate, Dr S. G. Rainsford said: 'The most disturbing factor ... is that the worker can be severely poisoned by lead without either having symptoms or showing clincial signs of plumbism. Probably the commonest early symptoms are abdominal discomfort, dyspepsia, loss of appetite and general aches and pains, the latter frequently being described as rheumatism, fibrositis, etc.

'In one series of 400 cases 5·25% of the workers complained of these symptoms ... and among these were 22 cases in whom pathological tests indicated with little doubt that they were suffering from lead poisoning. Only 6 of these cases had definite symptoms. In other words there were 16 cases of sub-clinical poisoning in a total of 22 in which the diagnosis could not have been made on clinical grounds alone.' ('The Problem of Medical Supervision of Lead Workers'—S. G. Rainsford, British Factory Inspectorate Medical Branch, 1965.)

In a medical situation as difficult as this, how many cases of sub-clinical lead poisoning are missed in general practice where lead is seldom, if ever, considered as a causative factor either in adults or children?

28. Although human city populations have not yet started to fall down because of lead poisoning, city animal populations are already dying. *Science* (vol 173: p 130, July 9 1971) reported that New York Medical College scientists had discovered that a large proportion of animals in Staten Island Zoo were suffering from severe lead poisoning. The death of several animals ranging from reptiles to leopards was attributed to lead fallout from heavy traffic. Those kept in outdoor cages were found to be most seriously affected.

29. There are good reasons for believing that these Medical Research Council figures were systematically low. Not only are they well below the contamination levels revealed as typical for busy streets in the US, but also below those indicated by a preliminary study carried out by Warwick in 1968 (J. Bullock and W. M. Lewis 'The influence of Traffic on Atmospheric Pollution': *Atmospheric Environment*: vol 2, pp 517–534, 1968). Curiously both the British studies used filtration systems too coarse to retain the biologically important small particles in a vehicle-produced aerosol, thus failing to record from 10% to 50% of the contamination.

30. The recent WHO decision to increase the permitted concentration of nitrates in drinking water from 10 ppm to 20 ppm in temperate countries also hints at non-public-health pressures. The change coincided with increasing concern about the effects of nitrates, both in rivers and in drinking water, yet facilitated the introduction of nitroso-triacetic acid (NTA) as a substitute base for detergents. NTA, which adds to nitrate burdens, is now discredited environmentally but the upward trend in the nitrate content of waters has been given further elbow room.

31. This point is omitted in the apparently thorough but reactionary report 'Airborne Lead in Perspective' (US National Research Council, National Academy of Sciences, 1971) which regards 0·8 ppm as 'acceptable' and minimizes the importance of sub-clinical effects. Even so this report's bland conclusions do not mirror the lack of knowledge and the implicit dangers revealed in its sections on children.

32. R. K. Byers and E. E. Lord: 'Late Effects of Lead Poisoning on Mental Development', *American Journal of Diseases in Children*, vol. 66, 5, 471–94, November 1943.

CHAPTER FOUR

ESSENTIAL AND DEADLY METALS

Mercury and lead share the undesirable characteristic of being not only deadly but entirely without any useful compensating function in biological systems when they turn up as contaminants. Their ubiquitous presence in living tissue is a reflection simply of their presence in the environment, not that of a cellular requirement. But this is by no means true of all heavy metals, some of which are just as essential to life as others are opposed. Even these serve their biological function satisfactorily only when they are present within fairly specific limits and in particular forms, so that either the deficiency or the over-abundance of an essential heavy metal can lead to disorders or to toxic effects. Further, similar metals tend to interfere with each other biologically, some lose their required biological activity in the presence of abnormal levels of other elements — such as sulphur — while others work in pairs even though concerned in a single biological function. In a very real way these essential metallic micro-nutrients can be regarded, like the vitamins, as recently discovered normal dietary constituents without which healthy life and growth is impossible. But, with the exception of the need for iron (haemoglobin) and for iodine (thyroid function), the understanding of the need for small amounts of metals in the diet is both less complete and more recent than that of the vitamins.

Broadly, then, a slowly growing understanding of the biological effects and roles of heavy metals has led to the growth of a parallel concern for their effects, even in very small amounts, on the patterns of health. The dawning truth is that environmental factors, with which the heavy metals are intimately involved, are responsible for a large but as yet undefined proportion of human and animal disease. The suggestion made, for instance, by the British geneticist, L. S. Penrose, in the 'fifties that the geographical variations in the incidence of congenital malformations of the central nervous system might suggest a causal agent 'such as the presence or absence of trace elements in the water supply'[1] has been amplified and broadened with time. In June 1970 the British medical journal *Lancet* stated in an editorial that the weight of evidence now suggested 'that environmental factors, as opposed to genetic ones, were primarily responsible for perhaps as much as 70–80% of human cancers,'[2] an assessment which in the United States rapidly gained currency. The number of cancer-causing agents is very large but, in terms of controllable environmental contaminants, the heavy metals comprise a significant proportion of them.

Again, during the 'sixties and in particular through the work of H. A. Schroeder at Dartmouth College, significant relationships were shown to exist between the levels of heavy metals in the diet and disease and, in the case of cadmium, with the incidence of high blood pressure and heart disease in the United States. Initially such relationships are often seen simply as statistical differences between hard and soft water areas, but the point underlying them is that the 'soft' or more acidic waters tend to dissolve metals more readily than alkaline waters. This kind of relationship, demonstrated in many countries during the 'sixties but not without some anomalies, was shown in 1971 to underlie the distribution pattern of the appalling nervous system malformation known as spina bifida in South Wales, where in some areas the incidence is two or three times higher than the national average. In this case, however, because of the complex interrelationship of the public water supply network and the resulting unreliability of data on local water quality, the authors conclude that the correlation that they have uncovered is 'probably secondary.'[3] The implication, again, is that trace-elements rather than water hardness are the real villains.

Perhaps the term 'trace-elements' needs some explanation. It comprises some 25–30 elements which, mainly metallic, were, because of the coarseness of analytical techniques, detected in amounts so small that they were described simply as 'traces' in early analyses of living tissues. In other words, although they were present, they were there in amounts below the limit of quantitative analysis. With advances in technique and in understanding of the biological roles of some metals, there has been a tendency in the English-speaking countries to refer to the essential metals as micro-nutrients, thus splitting off a small but as yet incomplete group from the others which are either benign or poisonous. This sounds tidy but may be misleading for, in nature, things tend to be much too complicated to be compressed into simplistic categories. Cross interference such as blocking or potentiating ability can, in differing circumstances, transfer a metal from one category to another. The micro-nutrient is capable of poisoning the system, and the toxic trace-elements are better tolerated in some circumstances than in others. One at least, arsenic, although traditionally regarded as the most potent of metallic poisons, is in fact of relatively low mammalian toxicity when compared to some of the other trace-elements, and in dietary experiments has been shown not only to be well tolerated at low dose levels but to actually increase the life-span of experimental animals.[4]

The toleration of 'normal' levels of toxic trace-elements is, of course, the evolutionary result of millions of years of living organism development in an environment in which the trace-elements are ubiquitous. Problems arise only when, either through natural variations in distribution or through man-made contamination, the 'normal' levels are in some way modified. By far the largest modifications are caused by human activities, through the burning of fossil fuel, for example, or through the extensive use in technology of naturally rare metals such as cadmium or beryllium. It is these activities, hitherto largely unconsidered in broad public health patterns, which need emphasis and examination.

THE AWAKENING

Yet, historically speaking, the accumulation of knowledge about trace-elements and their effects has run through two phases, neither of which has had any central concern with man-created contamination. The earliest studies were empirical investigations of widely dispersed nutritional maladies in domestic animals and man. It was in this phase, for example, that copper was first recognized as an essential requirement in mammals for growth and haemoglobin formation, that cobalt deficiency led to 'wasting diseases' of one kind and another in stock, that molybdenum could have a marked effect on copper uptake by cattle and that manganese deficiencies were associated with skeletal, muscular and neural malformation in birds. Following the much earlier recognition of iodine and iron as essential nutrients, these discoveries of the 'thirties led to the first serious attempts to evaluate the trace-elements singly as nutrients in laboratory experiments. Much of this work was, unfortunately, doomed to meaninglessness because of inadequate analytical techniques and the unknown presence of contaminants in the food and water used for experimental diets.

The second phase, backed by adequate techniques both for nutritional studies and, through radionuclides, for distribution and function studies, began in the late 'forties and is still going strong. Since iodine is a non-metal, it might reasonably be said that 50 years ago the only metal known to be an essential nutrient was iron. The picture now, and this is by no means necessarily a complete list, shows that cobalt, chromium, manganese, molybdenum, selenium and zinc are also certainly essential, and that nickel, rubidium and vanadium may have important significance in specific biological functions. Some scientists would include cadmium in the list of probables, because it occurs as a metallo-protein in most mammals. All scientists involved with this kind of research would support that notion that many trace-elements now believed to be inactive will in time be shown to have specific roles in living processes.

We are talking here about metallic elements which—if the detoxifying organs (the liver and kidneys) are excluded because their burdens of metals are anomalous—are performing active and essential biological roles at levels often much less than 0·01 ppm in the living cell. To be of such great importance at such low concentrations they must be associated with the function of enzymes, the so-called catalysts of life, either directly in the formation of the active sites of metallo-enzymes, or with the more loosely constructed co-enzymes. This explanation is certainly supported by biochemical studies, although the understanding of enzyme function at the molecular level is patchy to say the least. (The possible involvement of direct metal ion catalysis, of the kind used in the chemistry laboratory or the chemical industry, has been completely excluded, but a great deal has been done to explain how the presence of a metal ion can be of fundamental importance in determining the shape of a folded protein.) Yet, even accepting the role of trace-elements in enzyme function, and the enormous amount of research that has been directed at their isolation in functional roles, there are good grounds for believing that so far only the most obvious aspects of their activity have been uncovered.

Changes in many enzyme levels of an experimental animal can now be monitored with great accuracy, and it follows that it is possible to monitor enzymes which require a specific trace-element for the acquisition of biological activity. With the exclusion of an essential trace-element from the diet it would be expected that enzyme changes would necessarily precede the onset of clinical symptoms of deficiency disease. *Sometimes* this is the case. But in many experimental situations profound clinical disturbances occur either before enzyme changes become measurable, or entirely in their absence. This must mean that either there are many trace-element functional roles as yet uncovered, or that there are many more trace-element dependent enzymes in living systems than those known at the moment. Limits and inconsistencies in present knowledge must obviously be borne in mind when weighing the possible effects of trace-element combination.

Yet, if a great deal remains to be learned about trace-element function and toxicity in animals and plants, there are yawning gaps in present knowledge of trace-element water–soil–plant–animal interrelationships. Even when considering a single soil type, local water, a single plant species, one trace-element and one species of animal, the complexities are enormous. A host of variables, including the availability of major nutrients, climate and acidity, the state of maturity of both plant and animal, the availability of all other trace-elements and the form of other chemical elements, such as sulphur, have to be taken into the picture. In practice the situation is even more daunting for seldom if ever are relationships confined to single species. While deficiency diseases and symptoms of poisoning tend to show up fairly rapidly in animals such as sheep and cattle which are confined to specific areas, enormous variations of trace-element uptake can be produced by commonplace activities, such as fertilizer treatment of soil, for fertilizers may be insidiously rich in a potentially toxic trace-element, and in any case may lead to major changes in the pattern of plant growth. Different plants have different trace-element uptakes. Quite apart from leading to marked variations in the availability of trace-elements to a feeding animal, plants may also contain other biologically active compounds which block the utilization of important trace-elements within the animal.

It is not suprising that scientists concerned with the

role of trace-elements in nutrition are quite open in their belief that, while some fairly coarse relationships between deficiency or abundance and disease have been uncovered, there must exist an enormous range of clinically obscure and therefore undiscovered trace-element mediated conditions which are widespread and which have important bearings on growth, productivity and susceptibility to bacterial and other infections. In human beings the pattern of interrelationship with soils and plants is both much more complex and possibly less potentially dangerous than that of animals, although this is by no means certain.

PATTERNS AND DOSES

One basic argument is that, in developed countries with a complex national and international food marketing pattern, the average human diet is no longer dominated by local soil characteristics. While this is true, some important reservations have to be made. The proportion of local fresh vegetables in the diet clearly varies from season to season in those countries not yet overrun by the pre-packed, non-flavour, frozen-food type of technomania commodity, and although the seasonal variations may be fairly small in cities they are probably large in many rural areas even in the most developed countries. Further, although the complex pattern of food distribution may well tend towards balancing the normal human trace-element intake, this is not the only variable. A significant proportion of trace-element intake comes from water; the processing and handling of foodstuffs leads both to the elimination and to the enrichment of trace-elements, and dietary preferences especially for shellfish and for offal—such as liver and kidney—can in combination have a major impact on both area and individual trace-element patterns. The optimistic view is that, in the end, things more or less balance out, but it is obvious that in the case of any trace-element that is both toxic and accumulative, regional and personal variations can lead to trouble. Further, as *processing* becomes increasingly entrenched in nutritional patterns, the chances of deficiency diseases of one kind or another will increase proportionally.

So it can be seen that any simplistic interpretation of trace-element/diet/disease patterns is doomed to almost certain error, and that the complexities are probably too great for the patterns to be unravelled by present monitoring techniques and statistical disease analysis. Not only is it very probable that a large proportion of trace-element induced disease goes unrecorded as such simply because it is not recognized, but studies of trace-element distribution, both in soils and in diets, are at the present time so patchy as to provide an inadequate basis for epidemiological patterns and trace-element patterns to be usefully compared.

This is not always the case. In the United States, for example, death rates from cardiovascular diseases appear to be very strongly correlated with high concentrations of airborne cadmium and cadmium in milk,[5] a correlation which tends to be confirmed by the anomalously large amounts of cadmium in the kidneys of those dying of high blood pressure. On the other hand the extremely high mortality rate from spina bifida on the Atlantic coast of the United States[6]—almost three times that of the Pacific coast—remains completely unexplained. Similarly, regional variations in the incidence of particular types of cancer, and variations within regions between different social strata, while as yet unexplained, point firmly to environmental influences in which trace-elements almost certainly have an important role.

In the light of all this it is surprising, to say the least, that large scale integrated programmes for the determination of geographic variations of trace-element intake have not been initiated either nationally or internationally in any really determined way. Those holding the purse-strings of contamination and pollution studies are probably too involved with problems they can see only too clearly to be tempted into the expensive unravelling of problems that cannot be seen clearly at all. No nation has yet carried out the kind of comprehensive trace-element survey needed for the understanding of disease patterns, although many local studies have been initiated for medical and veterinary reasons (for example, copper, molybdenum, zinc, cadmium and mercury in relation to clinically obvious animal and human disease) and trace-element surveys in mineral exploration are now common-place but again so patchy as to be generally valueless from the medical point of view. Unfortunately the trace-element studies needed by those who wish to exploit the earth's resources do not, in any case, match those needed to understand or ameliorate human suffering.

Looked at simply in its practical aspects, trace-element surveying appears to be fraught with difficulties. To construct a reasonably detailed contour map of naturally occurring concentrations in the soil you need reliable samples at something like 1-mile intervals over the whole area of survey. To ensure reliability several samples would be required from a single site, preferably taken a few hundred yards apart and carefully chosen to eliminate transient effects such as fertilizer use. Each sample would then have to be subjected, preferably twice, to analysis for say 25 different trace-elements. So, even for a small country many millions of analyses and other operations would be required, and the cost would seem to far outweigh any practical advantage.

Yet in some circumstances detailed trace-element contour maps can be produced at surprisingly low cost. Indeed maps for some 20 trace-elements based on an approximate 1-mile grid for the whole of England and Wales are already being produced by the geochemical department of Imperial College in London. The overall cost turned out to be around £100,000 ($240,000) and although aimed primarily at those interested in mineral surveys, the technique used could well be modified to provide essential information for epidemiological studies. Low cost and, in this case success, both rest on the willing availability of skilled but inexpensive summer labour in the form of geological and geochemical students at universities throughout the country, and on the fact that the sediments formed over the years in the beds of streams provide naturally averaged samples of local trace-element concentrations. It just happens that in England and Wales (with the relatively insignificant exception of mountainous and marshy areas), stream and road or track intersections occur at roughly 1-mile intervals throughout the countryside. Given road access, simple equipment for collection and drying, expertise in sample point selection, standard ordnance survey grid references, high-speed automated analysis back at the Imperial College base, plus correlation, smoothing and plotting of data, the entire operation was completed within two years.

Obviously such a technique—which, incidentally, requires careful intermediate interpretation because leaching and deposition rates of many elements may vary with changes in local conditions such as acidity—can only be applied where both streams and roads are numerous. But suitable patterns exist in many European countries, in large areas of North America and in many other parts of the world. Even as it stands the British survey may turn out to be of great value as an indicator of regions requiring special investigation for medical reasons although, because of its essentially mining-orientated selection of trace-elements, much might be missed. Cadmium, for example, is not included in the survey and, since oven-drying of samples was employed in the field, it cannot provide reliable information about volatile but medically important trace-elements such as mercury. Yet the avoidance of these limitations is primarily a matter of technique involving little change in overall cost. The survey demonstrates what can be done with limited resources and, by the 'eighties, could form the basis of new and possibly revolutionary studies of disease.

METAL ON TAP

Yet, to be meaningful, surveys of this kind would need to be integrated with parallel surveys of the geographic distribution of trace-elements through public water supplies and air contamination. Studies of both are now beginning but only in a fragmented way, limited predominantly by the number of university research workers willing and able to take to the field. Official support is notably lacking and (if the experience of some British university investigators is taken as typical), can be fundamentally obstructive. Presumably water supply undertakings, subject tacitly if not legally to the recommended water standards of the World Health Organization but often unable to ensure their application, do not want publicity about potential hazards from the tap. That these probably exist is supported by the recent publication in Britain of a report of research undertaken by the Civil Engineering Department of Liverpool University.[7]

Using the World Health Organization International (1963) and European (1970) Standards for Drinking Water on an authoritative reference basis, public water supplies in 43 centres of population of over 100,000 were examined by means of samples taken directly from the tap in randomly selected houses. These were analysed for lead, cadmium, arsenic, selenium, chromium-6, cyanide and barium. The results for lead, already mentioned in Chapter 3, show that 13% of samples were above the International standard of 0·05 ppm and that a further 17% were at the limit. In one area the levels approached the upper limit of the new European standard (MAC of 0·1 ppm), suggesting that in this area water could add very significantly to lead burdens. A daily intake of 2 litres of water would, for example, add 200 micrograms of lead to the dietary intake, of which 10 to 30 micro-grams would be absorbed.

No less serious was the discovery that, although barium was at very low levels in all samples, the water of one city (Sheffield) was found to contain cadmium in amounts which exceeded the WHO maxima of 0·01 ppm. That Sheffield is a metal-working and plating centre *par excellence* suggests that purely local contamination might be responsible, but the important point arising from a limited survey of this kind is that large variations exist and that anomalously high levels are not always pre-vented by present routine controls. That these controls may be extremely primitive is emphasized by evidence submitted by the British Institution of Water Engineers to the Central Advisory Water Committee in 1970: '. . . frequently the first knowledge of pollution has been by visual observation (presumably during the hours of daylight) by the staff of the undertaking or by others. For any water undertaking to have to rely solely upon chance observation for the protection of a product so vital to the community would be courting disaster. If some of the recorded incidents of pollution, which were visually observed, had occurred during the hours of dark-ness or had otherwise been missed, the consequences could have been extremely serious.' Clearly, this refers to pollution which showed up as turbidity or discoloura-tion, and the 'others' are members of the public. In-visible pollutants like the heavy metals might show up by taste, but it is clear that they could all too easily escape detection.

This is a disturbing state of affairs. The 1971 report of the British Government-appointed technical committee on the disposal of solid toxic wastes[8] emphasizes that pollution of streams and rivers is far more common than the pollution of ground waters used for drinking supplies and that as far as was known at that time there had been no significant pollution due to tipped toxic wastes. But the incidents of drinking water pollution that are listed as typical were largely uncovered by complaints about 'taste', not by chemical monitoring systems. The analysis followed the distribution of tainted water which was not intercepted. Now the concentrations of heavy metals like selenium or cadmium likely to be of relevance to public health are so low that they would not be detected by taste. There is, incidentally, in the British toxic waste report, no indication of the extent or accuracy of analyses carried out after complaints were received. It is all too clear that monitoring, where it occurs on a continuous basis, is of an unsophisticated kind, and that often it is altogether too patchy or too primitive to keep pace with the exotic toxic wastes now reaching the land in increasing quantities.

It is relevant that the preferred disposal method for waste mercurials by some of the largest US manufacturers is that of 'exposure and erosion on waste land' and that in Britain old industrial waste dumps present some of the most intractable pollution problems from run-off. Lead, chromium-6, cadmium and nickel are among the metals involved and often the only practical course is that of covering and turfing the dump surface to reduce run-off. But in some circumstances, such as the increased rate of leaching caused by metal mining and quarrying in mountainous areas, the metallic content of run-off can be permanently increased and may in particular climatic conditions result in highly toxic pulses of water reaching an otherwise unpolluted water course, leading in turn to potentially serious pollution of estuarial waters.

Even though in the United States most of the recorded episodes of ground water contamination involve direct run-off from dumped wastes or the accidental recycling of detergent-rich sewage water, changes in the metal concentration of run-off must also exist in areas that have been worked for minerals. Certainly this has happened in Britain, sometimes with important consequences, although detection seems to be the result of circumstances which accidentally happen to be highly sensitive to metal-rich water. One of the most significant examples—significant that is in terms of its implications for productivity in estuaries and coastal waters, the nurseries of the sea—occurred in Wales during the period 1966–70.

YESTERDAY'S SHADOW

With the aim of revitalizing Britain's failing oyster production industry the White Fish Authority established an oyster hatchery at Conway, North Wales, in 1966. Using a tested scheme for hatching and larval production, the unit was set up under controlled commercial conditions using filtered estuary water for the tanks containing adult breeding stock, and filtered water in separate tanks for larvae released by the breeding stock. After rearing for about 8 weeks the larvae settle as spat and are transferred to growing trays in the shallow estuary. A continuous water flow is maintained in the breeding and growing tanks by pumping from an intake at the narrow river end of the tidal region.

Since the operating and growing conditions had been proved before the unit was established a 'settling' rate of spat of about 60% was expected as normal. Yet, in a curious and at first unexplained way, the unit suffered cyclic failures in which larval mortality was sometimes close to 100%. After three seasons of sporadic failure and a careful internal investigation which revealed nothing likely to cause such high mortality, a detailed and continuous examination of water quality was carried out by the geochemistry department at Imperial College. Metal contamination was already suspected because of earlier surveys of stream sediments in North Wales, an area which has been exploited for two centuries or more in mining operations that, generally, have been on a small scale.

In an estuary the salinity of the water varies cyclically with the tides both on a daily basis and on the basis of the lunar month, which determines tide height. It was discovered that, during the early months of the year (that is, the period most important in larva production), the expected tidal variations in nutrient contents of the hatchery water were accompanied by startling peaks in zinc concentration which rose regularly to around 500 micrograms per litre, more than 50 times the expected concentration. Similar, but much less marked peaks occurred in the lead concentrations.[9] Laboratory investigation soon showed that, at this level, zinc was fatal to larvae, while an analysis of the pattern of variation of metal concentration suggested that because of layering of fresh and saline water in the estuary some tidal conditions could lead to an unusually large proportion of metal-rich river water entering the hatchery intake. Metal concentrations in the river itself were shown to vary widely both from tributary to tributary and from month to month. A more or less conclusive correlation between high rainfall and old mine workings came fairly easily to light. Some of the water from mineralized areas was found to contain up to about 900 ppm zinc, over 7·0 ppm lead, and 2·5 ppm cadmium. It is clear that concentrations of this sort, caused by mining technology but reaching over the centuries, could produce serious consequences on the productivity of estuaries, on the quality of water supplies abstracted from the main rivers, and on any projects such as fish farming likely to be established in nearby coastal regions.

Just how extensively yesterday's technology is affecting today's marine productivity, or what areas are likely—by concentration through the marine food chain or in shellfish—to be useless for fishery development, is not known simply because nobody has yet looked. But in Britain (in work supported by the Natural Environment Research Council, and by universities) the first coastal pollution trace-element research was launched belatedly in 1969–70, as it was in Scandinavia, the US and the Mediterranean countries.

The importance of this kind of technology-induced

change in the natural leaching rate is considerable, because the changes are likely to be permanent or at least long-lived and quite impossible to remedy. True, without being opened up by workings, naturally metal-rich areas also produce metal-rich waters, but because of erosion and deposition over great lengths of time, the variations in metal concentrations above 'normal'—although of potential significance to public health—are not dramatic.

By far the most widespread cause of pulses—that is transient peaks of high concentration—of metal contamination, whether in rivers and estuaries or in the atmosphere, is industrial effluent. Just as the massive growth in industrial demand for water (150 tons per ton of steel, 100 tons per ton of newsprint, 40 tons per ton of refined fuel oil, for example) is the major cause of river-life extermination and of raw water shortage throughout the developed countries, so is it also the greatest threat to estuarial life and to the productivity of coastal waters.

That the dumping of sewage and other sludges off New York has virtually wiped out local marine life was one of the least surprising discoveries of 1970. In the same year, however, it was also discovered that apparently similar dumping in the better swept Thames estuary had produced remarkably little change in marine productivity. So, if you are prepared to overlook the ecological and economic absurdity of deliberately dumping land-produced organic waste into the sea instead of back on the land, it is apparently possible to continue present practices provided that the dumping sites are well chosen. From a trace-element point of view this is important because sewage sludges are generally fairly rich in a surprisingly wide variety of metals. The annual output from London contains metal contamination that totals 1000 tons, including mercury, lead, cadmium, selenium, chromium and nickel. Metal-rich sedimentary build up, possibly in areas quite remote from the dumping point, seems to be inevitable, given enough time. As in the case of old mine workings which have, as it were, leaned across the centuries to disrupt our plans, today's apparently cheap and convenient method of sludge disposal could very easily become a serious burden for future generations more desperate than are we for high coastal productivity.

That things are probably far from well in most estuaries and appalling in many are facts which, quite apart from official recommendations that they should be investigated (such as that of Britain's Standing Royal Commission on Environmental Pollution), have been thrown up by research in many parts of the world. Fjords on the Swedish coast have, like the Baltic, been shown to be excessively depleted in oxygen through the demands of effluent discharge, as have estuaries in Italy and on the Mediterranean coasts of France and Spain. But these studies are often not sophisticated enough to reveal trace-element imbalances or heavy metal contamination. Much more sinister is the discovery of mercury-rich estuarial regions in the Adriatic,[10] and of pulses of zinc, lead and cadmium in British estuaries, such as the Severn.

The Severn studies, although fragmental, may be of particular importance since they involved the continuous monitoring of water moving down the estuary. Part of normal thesis work, they were generated by Bristol University in the course of a visionary environmental research project called Sabrina (the Roman name of the Severn) intended as an intensive multi-disciplinary attack on the water dynamics, the ecology and present levels of contamination in this already considerably industrialized estuary. The project, although a research-trend leader in the UK, has received the cold shoulder of industry and only fragmental official support which has not been for the project as such, but for specific small experiments. It appears that, although enormous industrial development is planned for the area over the next decade, the information needed for planning aimed at minimal ecological disturbance is not available, and obstruction and lack of support may well combine to ensure that it will not be available in time. The Severn estuary is not unique. Simply because of the availability of water, massive estuarial developments are occurring throughout the world and often entirely without adequate environmental investigation. Time is running out.

NOBODY'S BABY

Scientifically and historically, the lack of adequate estuarial studies has arisen because estuary conditions fall into neither of the established areas of aquatic study —freshwater and marine. Dynamically and ecologically, estuaries differ widely, but they share the common fate of being used as open sewers for the disposal of all manner of untreated effluent. And they are dying. Even vast and biologically rich brackish areas like Chesapeake Bay (which might seem large enough to digest any insult), are seriously threatened. But any meaningful evaluation of the situation, whether designed to define present environmental conditions and hazards, or to delineate safe latitudes for industrial development, requires a very expensive investment of skilled manpower. Marine biologists cannot work alone in these regions where land and freshwater meet the sea and tidal action. They need the support of freshwater biologists, chemists and biochemists, hydrographers, sedimentologists and geochemists. Industry cannot or will not mount such operations and it is only just dawning on Governments that, for survival, they are essential.

In most cases even the most elementary facts, such as the dynamic salinity patterns, are not known. Yet these are regions on which marine productivity rests and which are nevertheless subjected to the slow and tidally oscillating clearance of enormous quantities of toxic contaminants. The Bristol studies of the Severn revealed, for example, that tidally compressed pulses of metal-rich water moved very slowly down toward the open sea, passing and repassing the same monitoring point several times before moving on. Initial studies showed in 1970 that peak simultaneous concentrations of 150 micrograms per litre of zinc, 15 micrograms per litre of cadmium and concentrations of lead and mercury in the range of 2·5 to 1·0 micrograms per litre, were common. The implications, both for marine productivity and for humans through the contamination of otherwise valuable seafood, are enormous, yet virtually no fabric of knowledge exists on which even to begin to build interpretations. That Bristol University discovered shellfish containing up to 550 ppm (dry weight) of cadmium (compared to 6·0 in the English Channel) is an indication of the seriousness of the situation.

These are dangerously high levels and they occur in a region already to some extent involved in shellfish production. One of the worrying features is not simply that such large accumulations can occur from transient pulses of metallic contamination, but that virtually nothing is known of the effects of such pulses on estuarial ecology or on individual organisms. Shellfish obviously do not stop feeding in the face of this kind of contamination, so the often-expressed if highly cynical view that the occasional cloud of turbid pollution does not matter, clearly does not apply.

THE POISON PULSE

The possible effects on food chains and on the toxicity of commerical yields is at the present time unknown, but research at Glasgow University has uncovered some remarkable primary effects. In the laboratory it has been shown that quite low levels of organic mercurials can seriously affect the growth rate of algae even when exposure is transient. A reduction of 50% in growth rate over 3 weeks results from only $17\frac{1}{2}$ minutes exposure to alkyl mercuric chlorides at a concentration of only 0·08 ppm, or from a 25-minute exposure at half that concentration, 0·04 ppm. The effect is clearly not linear and suggests that severe inhibition could occur from repeated exposure at much lower levels, even when these are of quite short duration. *Indeed tidal oscillation of toxic pulses seems likely to produce deleterious effects that are out of all proportion to those indicated by lethality studies.*

Now, as has been pointed out before, estuaries and the narrow bands of coastal water are the nurseries of the sea, and it can be seen from these results that massive changes in growth and survival rates and in the structure of food chains could be and, in many areas, are being caused by extremely low levels of contamination. To obtain any kind of response either from public health authorities or from agencies controlling industrial or domestic effluent it is often necessary to demonstrate that something is obviously damaging and that areas are dying off. Since estuaries do not fall directly under any single consent-granting authority and are not wholly subject to river authority control, they have been exploited to the verge of extinction. It seems incredible that, having permitted and later regretted the insane destruction of salmon rivers through both pollution and water course interference, we are now allowing a massive extension of the same kind of destruction.

Simply because of laxity through default of effluent control, *the most potentially corrosive of industries,* such as smelting and heavy chemicals, have concentrated and are now proliferating in *precisely those regions most sensitive to contamination.* Yet on the basis of existing knowledge their effects are entirely unpredictable but can only be damaging. The authorities most likely to produce powerful arguments for close control, those concerned with public health, have little voice when a proposal is made to pipe toxic wastes, such as cyanides or heavy metals, a mile out into an estuary. Yet the actual investigations proposed and carried out by industry and supposed to ensure environmental safety are often derisory. Further, initial consents discussed in detail at public investigations and assumed to be final, are often modified and extended without public consultation and without any investigation at all. The details of this kind of malignant growth are, through the nature of statutes, particularly in Britain, wrapped up in the traditional secrecy that surrounds the dealings of such bodies as the Alkali Inspectorate, the departments of Health, Agriculture and Fisheries and regional medical officers of health. They emerge from time to time in the discussions of local government where, inevitably, the most powerful influences are those of development, economic growth and authority boundaries.

In spite of protestations of concern, the official and industrial view appears still to be that provided stacks are high enough and pipes are long enough dilution will be adequate and, in any case, somebody else will get the effluent. How else is it possible to explain the seemingly underhand trebling of permitted fluorine effluents from a plant such as the aluminium smelter at Holyhead in Anglesey, North Wales? This was an incredible development itself for it was carried through in the face of almost total public opposition in an area designated as of 'outstanding natural beauty.' How else can we explain the sheer environmental insolence of such proposals as that to pipe 400,000 gallons a day of cyanide-rich waste into the Severn Estuary? Dispersal has been weighed under only one set of tidal conditions: ecological consequences remain unknown, but the persuasive economic arguments of developers seem often to be blindly overpowering.

All this might seem rather remote from the consideration of trace-elements, but if the resolution of quite coarse industrial or social impacts on the environment is often highly unsatisfactory, what chance is there for sensitive and environmentally sound handling of the immensely subtle problems of trace-element distribution? The scale of industrial plants is escalating rapidly, the complexity of effluents and of their catalyst content is growing and, if local pollution problems are to be avoided, the next two decades will witness the increasing exploitation of remote disposal of toxic materials by pipeline into large estuaries or into the sea. Just as the 19th and early 20th century saw the gradual extinction of rivers in industrialized areas, so could the late 20th century be watching the beginning of the extinction of the seas. Since much of the toxic waste now dumped at sea under industrial contract is handled in that way because municipal treatment plants cannot cope with it, or could cope with it at costs greater than those industry is willing to meet, and because much of this waste is rich in a whole range of metals, the need for an adequate knowledge of their biological fate and effects is of growing urgency.

Monitoring services, such as those being established slowly on both a national and international basis are simply not enough. The ability to predict effects and to enforce recovery and recycling when necessary is essential. If, as we are now aware, the continual presence of a few dietary micrograms of a toxic trace-element can have marked effects on human and animal health, what are we to expect to result from the disposal of massive quantities of metallic wastes in the sea, an environment already demonstrated to be highly sensitive to their presence? In a word, the answer may be disaster.

METALLIC MAZE

This is a context which has to be weighed, not in terms of biodegradability like the disposal of organic wastes which, within natural limits, can be coped with harmlessly, but in terms of the utmost persistence, like organochlorine pesticides and related compounds. True, in terms of industrial effluents and potential toxicity, the number of metals involved may not be high. Lead, mercury, cadmium, selenium, nickel and chromium, all of which are common in plating, plastic, metal-working and chemical effluents, are those most in need of examination. And it is not only through liquid effluents that they reach the environment in quantity. Some are natural airborne contaminants mainly as dust from soil, and although the major trace-elements in this group—aluminium, barium, iron, strontium and titanium—occur in relatively large amounts and have been shown to accumulate to some extent in lung tissue, none appear to be actively poisonous. Iron is, of course, essential, but the amount absorbed through the lung is small compared to that of the diet and is hardly more than a useful addition.

The natural airborne contaminants, however, present a much wider range of metallic elements, some of which are essential, some benign and some hazardous. Of those which are essential the burning of fossil fuels creates an airborne source of cobalt, copper, chromium, manganese, molybdenum, selenium and zinc. In general the amounts are small but one of these metals, selenium, although essential, is non-toxic only below strictly limited levels of intake. Recent research suggests that it may be accumulating in the environment to a much greater extent than has hitherto been believed, a point which will be taken up later.

With the exception of petrol which contains virtually only the contaminants deliberately added (for the cracking process leaves metals in the lower fractions), petroleum products result in air pollution from arsenic, nickel, niobium, mercury, vanadium, yttrium and zirconium. Most of these, with the addition of chromium, beryllium, germanium, tin, titanium and considerably larger amounts of mercury, also reach the air from coal, while industrial processes such as smelting result in the release of significant quantities of antimony, lead, tin and cadmium. Many of these metals, although toxic, are at the moment present in air in amounts that are so small that they produce no significant increase in the quantity absorbed by animals and humans. Some, however, because they are carcinogenic or are present in greater concentration, are already being seen as potential public health hazards. Mercury and lead we already know about, and to these we need to add antimony, arsenic, beryllium, cadmium, nickel and selenium. In a general assessment in 1971[11] Professor H. A. Schroeder singled out cadmium as 'a present and real hazard' and nickel as a potential but real hazard.

While this is probably the best assessment of the present situation in both the US and Britain, where Government and other public health and monitoring laboratories began to shape up their analytical systems for cadmium in the early 'seventies, there are good reasons for looking hard at the other metals. Antimony, for example, widely used in lead alloys for battery plates and type metal, perhaps best known in the form of 'tartar emetic' (potassium antimony tartrate), but also widely employed as flame retardant in paints and textiles, in the compounding of rubber and in ceramic glazes—has some mysterious and potentially hazardous biological properties. It is not simply that in dietary studies in small mammals it has been shown to shorten life-span at extremely low concentrations,[12] but that it possesses unpredictable and sometimes fatal effects on both the heart and the liver at dose levels well below those normally regarded as poisonous.[13] Since there have been virtually no detailed studies of this phenomenon, nor of the interactive effects of antimony with other metals, nor indeed of its effects or fate in biological systems, antimony is in need of careful examination. The highly toxic gas called stibine (antimony hydride, SbH_3) is evolved during the charging of storage batteries and it seems very likely that human exposure to both this and to the metal in many other forms, may be much wider than is generally believed. Like cadmium it could well be locally involved in areas where cardiac diseases are anomalously high, although no work has been done to establish whether or not such a correlation exists.

That antimony is a far more extensive contaminant than would be expected from the normally close control required of industry, was revealed in 1970 by the publication of the analyses of sea birds killed in the massive mysterious 'wreck' in the Irish Sea in 1969. In a surprising and disturbingly large number of samples of liver and kidney, antimony was found to be present in concentrations ranging from 40 ppm to over 400 ppm.[14] The tremendous variation of concentrations, with an upper range which might itself be close to the lethal threshold, points to industrial contamination and marine 'hot-spots' whose existence had previously been unsuspected. Since marine species are not normally monitored for antimony content, the meaning of these findings in terms of human nutrition is completely obscure.

No one knows the long-term effects of antimony, nor understands its extraordinary power to disrupt the function of cardiac muscle. Similarly food chain concentrations and effects are not known and nobody has taken a serious look. Because its general toxicity has been appreciated for the best part of two centuries, industrial environments involving antimony are carefully controlled, yet large amounts are demonstrably reaching the seas. Since once it is in the environment and in, say, marine sediments, it is—like other metals—there for ever, the now obvious failure to maintain adequate control could mean that serious local contamination problems already exist. Yet there are no obvious signs that this is appreciated either by Government agencies or by industry.

SELENIUM-PLUS

Similar considerations may well also apply to selenium, a metal which, although essential, is very highly toxic. In animal nutrition studies selenium and arsenic are necessarily considered together, for arsenic blocks the toxic action of selenium. Their relative toxicities give some idea just how poisonous selenium can be. In mammals the dose of arsenic which will kill half of the animals receiving it within 24 hours (24 hr LD50) is around 40 milligrams per kilogram of body weight: the 24 hr LD50 for selenium (as sodium selenite) is a mere 4 micrograms per kilogram of body weight. *Selenium, at least in some circumstances, is ten thousand times as poisonous as arsenic.* (LD50 = Lethal Dose 50%).

Since its general mammalian toxicity is low it may therefore not seem to matter that arsenic is very widespread in soils (10 ppm to 40 ppm over most of the earth's surface), and there are clearly some selenium-rich areas in which the presence of arsenic is biologically beneficial. Indeed since the discovery in the 'fifties that some very serious and widespread animal diseases were in fact selenium poisoning ('alkali disease' in the US and the 'blind staggers' in New Zealand) arsenic has taken on a new and very important role as a disease controlling agent. The discovery of very high levels of arsenic in shellfish off European coasts (147 ppm in prawns in British waters) is, in general, not regarded as a problem. Unfortunately, although arsenic may be genuinely good for you in some circumstances even in such apparently high concentrations, there are signs that this may not always be the case.

Experiments carried out in Russia have indicated, for example, that some kind of synergism exists between arsenic and lead.[15] Although in general less toxic than lead, arsenic appears either to increase its own toxicity or that of lead itself when both metals are present at the same biological site. As in the case of many metallic toxic effects, this synergism is neither understood nor even the subject of investigation. A similar state of affairs surrounds other at present mysterious potentiating effects, such as that of copper on the toxicity of mercury.

The biological implications of that particular relationship have, however, been grasped, which perhaps renders it less important in this context than the fact that, in the case of selenium, there is open ignorance of direct toxic effects, and equally open ignorance of its fate or concentration-effects in biological systems. Since selenium is almost universally present as an air contaminant from fossil fuels, and since it is accepted as being considerably more poisonous than mercury, this ignorance is astounding. It was brought sharply to light in 1971 at the annual meeting of the American Chemical Society when Dr R. A. Copeland revealed that large amounts of selenium had been found in zooplankton in Lake Michigan, downwind of Chicago.[16] Something of the toxicity of selenium can be gathered from the UN and the US Federal maximum allowable concentration in drinking water of 0·01 ppm, although even this apparently low level may turn out to be overlax. For the discovery of selenium in the range 0·1 to 1·2 ppm in zooplankton, reported by Dr Copeland, indicates either a much larger fallout of the metal than had been suspected, or an unsuspected but highly efficient concentration mechanism in lower aquatic organisms.

Not surprisingly the high selenium levels appear, in the case of Lake Michigan, to correlate with fallout from Chicago, but this fallout region is large and carries possibly serious implications for other areas. On the basis of existing knowledge and standards an upper limit of selenium in fish for human consumption might be set at around 0·25 ppm wet weight. The zooplankton levels suggest that this could easily be exceeded in some freshwater fisheries, but the truth is that at the moment no one knows the effects of selenium on aquatic life, its concentrations in fish, or the chemical forms in which it concentrates.

The chemistry and biochemistry of selenium is inevitably very complicated, but because the metal is so very poisonous to man (and other animals) at least the basic questions need to be answered as a matter of urgency. It might turn out that the forms in which it concentrates in plankton are not particularly toxic, or that they are relatively benign and—higher up the food chain—have such a short half-life that no significant concentrations occur. Optimists might argue that since there has been no trouble in the past as far as we know, this is probably the case. But it seems wiser to find out rather than wait for trouble for, if selenium is a potent depressor of lower organism growth or if it does concentrate in fish or, indeed, in crops through surface absorption, then it could be as serious a threat to the life cycle as organic mercury. We need to find out.

BERYLLIUM-AIRED

No less serious, although the metal is perhaps industrially better documented and controlled, are the implications of beryllium contamination. Again food chain fates of the metal are unknown, a situation which, until the last couple of decades, hardly mattered for very little is naturally mobilized. But with the proliferation of the nuclear industry its use in canning and other components has expanded rapidly and the possibility of contamination has proliferated. As a dust it causes lung cancer, and beryllium dust has been identified in several urban areas of the United States, and in at least four non-urban areas. All are associated with smelting, with the nuclear industry, with nuclear testing or (in the past) with fluorescent lamp production. At the outset of its industrial use the potency of beryllium as a cancer-causing agent was seriously underestimated, a tragic error which resulted in a wave of beryllium-induced industrial deaths. Even in the late 'sixties a British industrial hygienist wrote that there was much room still for the education of those who handle it,'[17] an understatement which ought to strike a chill of fear into those employed in beryllium handling industries. True, past errors have led to increased caution, but the lessons, as seems always to be the pattern, have been learned the hard way.

That a public health hazard, as distinct from an industrial occupation risk, existed in the case of beryllium came to light in the US in 1949 when the Atomic Energy Commission discovered that one of its large beryllium plants was leading to airborne contamination at concentrations up to 0·1 micrograms per cubic metre as much as three quarters of a mile away.[18] That does not sound serious, but investigation uncovered 10 cases of beryllium poisoning, one fatal, among residents of the area not employed at the factory. Very low concentrations were clearly more toxic than anyone believed. Indeed, under Britain's Alkali Inspectorate, the maximum concentration of beryllium allowed *at the point of effluent discharge* is now 0·1 micrograms per cubic metre, and discharge is normally from a high stack so that dilution occurs before the effluent reaches ground level.

Even so, it needs to be asked whether this is strict enough. Analysis of the likely public exposures in the AEC poisonings suggests that the accumulation of only a few micrograms of beryllium in lung tissue may, in time, lead to malignant changes in cells. Further, it seems that as with organic mercury, some individuals are much more sensitive than others although there is insufficient evidence to indicate whether infants and young children are more susceptible. Prudence dictates that, until it is proved otherwise, it should be assumed that children are sensitive and that, since beryllium deposits in the lungs appear to be permanent, an early deposit is more likely to cause trouble than one gathered later in life. Since neither may lead to disease until very late in life, important epidemiological statistics have yet to be gathered.

Exactly as in the case of organic mercury, beryllium is a metal that you do not want at any price. Yet, because of industrial pressures and the costs of its complete removal at the outlet points of industrial air-conditioning systems, it is already reaching the atmosphere in small amounts and may all too easily become widespread as a contaminant. Beryllium alloys have important engineering qualities which are likely to rapidly promote their use in industries not experienced in their handling, and to the accidental proliferation of beryllium contaminated wastes capable of eroding and leading to both air and water pollution. At the moment only those sites handling beryllium in large amounts are continuously monitored for fallout. Already this may not be good enough.

With the addition of chromium, again a cancer producing agent, we now have several metals known to be present as air contaminants but not widely monitored. Chromium is industrially notorious because of the great problems it poses to those trying to eliminate it from gaseous effluents, a point that suggests a more widespread contamination pattern than either industrialists or controlling agencies like to pretend. Yet, to establish continuous air contaminant monitoring systems sensitive enough to pick up airborne metals at the concentrations likely to be encountered—a few parts per billion—seems to be economically out of the question. Certainly, if thought about in terms of complex, automated, carefully engineered 'sniffing' systems, or as highly refined automatic spectroscopy of the kind likely to peer down at us from satellites, the costs of detecting, determining and continuously monitoring the range of metals and the other toxic burdens of the air of urban-industrial complexes would be totally prohibitive. Fortunately nature has provided other methods.

NATURAL MONITORS

Just as in the marine environment there are certain organisms which, because they are highly efficient at concentrating metals, can be used as pollution indicator species, so do some plants rapidly concentrate metals from the atmosphere. Indeed some kinds of moss are much more efficient at this than anything man has yet devised. Their unique properties as a kind of ion exchange resin capable of concentrating at very high efficiency all metallic elements were first exploited as a means of assessing contamination by scientists in Sweden who, alerted by the mercury problem, decided to survey the whole country for airborne contaminants.[19] Such a task might seem virtually impossible, but the value of indigenous natural 'sniffers', continually concentrating airborne metals, meant that long-averaged samples of metallic exposure could be obtained simply by analysing judiciously selected samples of one common species of moss. Air contamination gradients discovered by this method in Sweden showed that, in all probability, the major sources of airborne metallic contamination lay outside the country's own borders, thus raising a controversy about Europe's high industrial chimney philosophy that will not be easily or cheaply resolved.

True, the beginnings of international pollution monitoring systems have been laid by the International Biological Programme, by concerned sub-committees of the UN and, in the case of oil, by maritime organizations, but there exists a long rough road from the international ideals of scientists to the harsh economics of scrubbers in industrial stacks. The notable failure in Britain, for instance, to produce a dramatic drop in SO_2 pollution in spite of the stringent Clean Air Acts is almost entirely due to the universal industrial acceptance of the high stack philosophy. If you keep your detectors on the ground near the offending plant and then pump the effluent gases through a tall stack at high velocity, you can pretend that the fallout is small. Somebody else gets it and if, in these more enlightened days, the PR boys no longer crack jokes about the 'fallout hitting Moscow,' they still claim that dilution factors lead to safety and to great economic savings through the elimination of the need for SO_2 scrubbers. The real costs, through building erosion, extra cleaning, dangers to public health and changes in soil acidity (not to mention the value of reclaimed sulphur) are, in Europe particularly, still excluded from industry's budgets.

This is, perhaps, a story in itself, but it has relevance because it reveals a highly dangerous attitude to pollutants that is still tolerated by official thinking. Hence the great potential value of such simple techniques as moss analysis, for, with skill and care, these can be buttoned up by small and independent investigators—such as university departments—to serve as watchdogs in areas where no official watchdogs exist or, perhaps more sinister, where they exist but tell us nothing.

The use of the moss *Hypnum cupressiforme* took a significant step forward in the period 1969–71 when, with some aid from Britain's financially starved Natural Environment Research Council, the botany department at Swansea University carried out a survey along transects through the valley upwind of the urban industrial complex in South Wales and, as a control, along the relatively clean Gower peninsula.[20] Having been deeply involved for several years in the contamination and revegetation problems posed by old metal-rich and potentially dangerous soil heaps in the South Wales region and, less directly, with Sweden's programme of research in metal contamination, the unit was, and remains, among the very few capable of pushing the work forward.

Two aspects of the findings are of great importance. The first concerns metal contamination itself: in an area greater than 32 km in diameter (the limit of the survey) the metal content of the air around the complex was significantly high in zinc, copper, lead, cadmium and nickel, with several but completely unexplained peaks of both cadmium and copper. One area, in which sporadic cattle sickness had occurred for years and where a horse had recently died ostensibly from 'lead poisoning,' was found to be startlingly rich in cadmium (parallel analyses showed 9·9 ppm (dry weight) Cd in the grass and 330 ppm (wet weight) in the kidney of the horse). In other places the metal profile of individual industrial plumes could be detected by increased fallout for many kilometres. On a purely qualitative basis the contamination of the area was both more serious and more widespread than had been suspected. Further, tentative analyses in the quite separate but apparently much cleaner urban-industrial complex around Bristol revealed that conditions there were, if anything, worse than those around Swansea. Indeed, taken together with Swedish findings and with those of the few surveys carried out in the US, it confirmed that airborne metal contamination is likely, everywhere in the world, to be more serious than any official assessment concedes. The second major aspect of these findings concerns the technique itself: moss is sensitive to SO_2 and there therefore exist 'moss and lichen deserts' in many areas in and around urban industrial complexes. But it was found that, provided moss can be kept moist, its ion-exchange efficiency remains undiminished even when it is no longer growing. This means that it is possible to develop techniques in which known and relatively clean moss fragments, suspended in nylon net or some similar container, can be deployed in any area. Combined with laboratory standardization so that accumulation rates can be related to air concentration (by no means an unsurmountable step), a very simple and efficient method can be developed for the quantitative assessment of airborne contaminants. Further, because exposure can be anything from a week to several months, long-term averaged assessments will result, and these are important for ecological and for epidemiological studies. A revolution in air pollution monitoring is at hand for this method lies well within the financial reach of municipalities, colleges and even relatively small communities. The only real costs are those of standard laboratory analyses on equipment which every university possesses.

Obviously this is no more than a fragment of the beginning of biological monitoring systems of this kind (lichens are already in experimental use for the detection of low levels of SO_2 pollution), but its importance lies in its potential. No public medical authority and no agricultural authority in the world possesses detailed distribution analyses of trace metal fallout: none of the plans for better control of industrial emissions will result, on their present basis, in the unravelling of airborne distribution data; and no scheme of monitoring, even that implicit in the priorities of the US Environment Protection Agency, can hope to match the flexibility and sensitivity inherent in the use of widely distributed natural concentrators of contaminants. A silent universal network already exists to oversee the official watchdogs and to retain the indelible record of pollution patterns that, at the moment, are neither seen nor considered. It is up to us to use that network, and to see that its messages are properly interpreted.

However, this is a diversion—if an important one—from the metals themselves. Of the short list of 8 contaminants of special danger, two remain. These are cadmium and nickel. Both are too hazardous to be dismissed briefly, so they get the next chapter to themselves.

EPILOGUE

It should now be apparent why ecologists . . . and other environmental scientists wince when industrialists talk about the pollution carrying capacity of inland waters as 'a great natural resource' or when government officials caution against making water pollution standards too high for fear of 'discouraging industry.'

The true costs of our environmental destruction have never been subjected to proper accounting. The credits are localized and easily demonstrated by the beneficiaries, but the debits are widely dispersed and are borne by the entire population through the disintegration of physical and mental health; and, even more importantly, by the potentially lethal destruction of ecological systems. Despite social, economic and political barriers to proper ecological accounting, it is urgent and imperative for human society to get the books in order.

> Paul and Ann Ehrlich.
> Population: Resources: Environment.

This is as true of the 'great natural resource' of the atmosphere as it is of inland waters and estuaries. But in waterways the presence of pollution is all too readily seen and its destination known. The invisible contaminants of the air are not channelled and their fallout and biological fate is less closely confined. Accounting is therefore even more difficult. But, in spite of additional difficulty, the urgency is no less great. The first priority must go to the gathering of information for, without information, accounting of any kind is impossible.

Notes and References

1. L. S. Penrose: *Journal of Mental Deficiency Research*, vol 1:4, 1957.

2. 'Cancer Prevention,' Editorial article, *Lancet*, vol 1:1378, June 1970.

3. C. R. Lowe and others: 'Malformations of the Central Nervous system and Softness of Local Water Supplies,' *British Medical Journal*, vol 2:357–61, May 1971.

4. H. A. Schroeder and others: Arsenic, Germanium, Tin and Vanadium in Mice, etc, *Journal of Nutrition*, 92:245–52, 1967.

5. H. A. Schroeder: 'Trace Elements in the Human Environment.' *The Ecologist*, vol 1:11, May 1971.

6. D. Hewitt: *British Journal of Preventative and Social Medicine*, vol 17:13, 1963.

7. C. D. Reed and J. A. Tolley: 'Hazards from the Kitchen Tap,' *Journal of the Royal College of General Practitioners*, vol 21:13, 1971.

8. Disposal of Solid Toxic Wastes: report of the technical sub-committee on the disposal of solid toxic wastes. Command 4585: Her Majesty's Stationery Office, London, 1971.

9. H. Elderfield, L. Thornton and J. S. Webb: 'Heavy metals and oyster culture in Wales,' *Marine Pollution Bulletin*, vol 2:3, March 1971.

10. J. U. L. and S. Kitamura: 'Mercury in the Adriatic,' *Marine Pollution Bulletin*, vol 2:4, April 1971.

11. Schroeder. (See note 5.)

12. H. A. Schroeder and others: Zirconium, Niobium, Antimony and Fluorine in Mice, etc. *Journal of Nutrition*, 95:95–101, May 1968.

13. See, for example, E. Browning: *Toxicity of Industrial Metals* (Butterworth: second edition) 1969, p 26 onward.

14. 'The seabird Wreck of 1969 in the Irish Sea,' supplement on analytical and other data, edited M. W. Holdgate, Natural Environment Research Council, 1971.

15. 'Arsenic-lead Synergism,' Ministry of Health, Moscow USSR 1969 (translated *Journal of Hygiene and Sanitation*. vol 34:123, 1969).

16. R. A. Copeland and others: 'Selenium in zooplankton, Lake Michigan,' Proceedings of the 161st Annual Meeting, American Chemical Society, 1971.

17. D. Hunter: *The Diseases of Occupations* (English University Press, fourth edition); 1969, p 437.

18. M. Eisenbud and others: *Journal of Industrial Hygiene*, vol 31:282, 1949.

19. A. Ruhling and G. Tyler: 'Regional differences in the Deposition of Heavy Metals over Scandinavia,' *Journal of Applied Ecology*, vol 8, no 2, pp 497–508, August 1971.

20. G. T. Goodman and T. M. Roberts: 'Plants and Soils as Indicators of Metals in Air,' *Nature*, vol 231:5301, June 1971.

CHAPTER FIVE

CADMIUM CARDIACS AND A NICKEL FOR CANCER

Cadmium is highly poisonous, poorly understood bio-logically, grossly under-investigated as an environmental contaminant, but widely dispersed. As a natural component of soils and water it is present only in very low concentrations but its industrial uses are expanding explosively. World production of the metal has increased fourfold in the last 20 years (FIG. 5:1). In 1957 Scandinavian toxicologists declared emphatically that 'cadmium has probably more lethal possibilities than any of the metals,'[1] an assessment which, in spite of rapidly mounting evidence of chronic health injuries to workers in cadmium-rich environments, appears to have been largely ignored in terms of potential public health hazards.

Chronic exposure to relatively large amounts (and large in this context means a few parts per million in the diet or in the atmosphere) may after a number of years lead to an appallingly painful and commonly fatal affliction in which the skeleton decays and collapses. But the public health issues rest on a number of biological properties which appear to be not only unique to cadmium, but which are operative at the much lower exposure levels likely to be encountered by the general population in industrialized societies. So far, monitoring of diets and of the atmosphere for cadmium has been so patchy that it is impossible to define exposure levels. Where investigations have been made the wide variations or 'scatter' of concentrations in food, water and air show with certainty that the situation is more serious than public health authorities, captains of industry or governments pretend.

One unique property of cadmium is that it is accumulated with enormous efficiency in the kidneys of mammals where it becomes bound as a metallo-protein and is released and excreted only extremely slowly. New-born infants are virtually cadmium-free but kidney concentrations rise with age so that there exists a growing reservoir within the body from which small amounts increas-

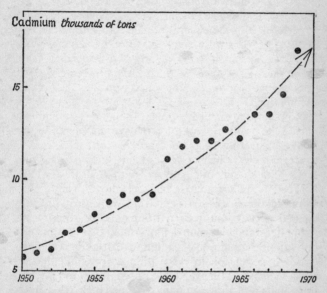

FIG. 5:1. World production of cadmium doubled between 1950 and 1960, and doubled again in the decade between 1960 and 1970. According to the present trend about 50,000 tons a year will be produced by 1980. Production is related to zinc smelting. Zinc production is increasing at a slower rate, an indication that cadmium recovery during zinc smelting is far from efficient.

ingly reach the bloodstream. Another property—which appears to be unique and which has been revealed experimentally in small mammals—is that at extremely low doses the injection of cadmium into the bloodstream produces an immediate increase of blood pressure.[2] No lower limit was demonstrated in these experiments but, translated into human terms, they indicate that an increase in blood pressure might be expected to result from the daily ingestion of only a few hundred micrograms of cadmium. Curiously, at higher doses, the metal produces the reverse effect—that is a reduction of blood pressure—which may partially explain why industrial hygienists observing comparatively large exposures failed to spot the metal's possible crucial role in the production of hypertension in the general population. *This is precisely the kind of oversight which makes it extremely dangerous for public health authorities to translate into public health terms the coarse findings which result from the study of occupational exposure.* The effects of metals are not predictable.

However, the extremely potent role that cadmium may play in the production of human hypertension, and hence in the staggering preponderance of cardiac disease in modern society, has been gradually unravelled in the United States and principally by one man, Professor H. A. Schroeder, at Dartmouth College, Hanover, New Hampshire. In the early 'sixties, having with great difficulty created a cadmium-free environment for experimental animals, he and his group demonstrated that in controlled conditions the addition of cadmium to drinking water produced hypertension in rats within a year, and that the effect increased with age.[3] Once raised, the blood pressure in animals receiving cadmium remained high, while in the cadmium-free control groups of animals blood pressure remained normal throughout life.

One of the striking features of this series of experiments was that the pattern of cadmium-induced hypertension in rats was remarkably similar to that prevalent among humans. Although the incidence was higher among females than males, the number of deaths with hypertension was higher among males than females. Not only was the life-span of the animals receiving cadmium about 20% shorter than that of the cadmium-free controls, but high blood pressure was accompanied by such typically human symptoms as enlargement of the heart, excess lipids and arterial sclerosis of the kidneys.[4] As might be expected, the kidney cadmium accumulations of these animals were much higher than those of controls, but not dissimilar to those of middle-aged Western men.

Professor Schroeder's group later showed that, in experimental animals, cadmium-induced hypertension could be reduced to normal by the administration of a zinc chelating agent although, after its experimental reduction, high blood pressure returned in some animals within a few months.[5] In human terms this may be important in that, in some circumstances, the potentially damaging effects of cadmium may somehow be ameliorated by the presence of large amounts of zinc—the metal with which cadmium is normally associated. However, by the time this work was published (1968) scientists in a number of countries had shown that there existed a positive correlation between the softness of drinking water and the incidence of heart disease.

One characteristic of soft water, as has already been mentioned, is the ability to dissolve metals more readily than hard water. Yet, while the distribution of metals in this way has hardly been studied, those studies that have been carried out—at least in England and Wales—have failed to show any immediately obvious correlation between heart disease and variations of a few parts per billion in cadmium content of municipal water. This is perplexing and such findings, which provide valuable delaying ammunition for those wishing to minimize the dangers of cadmium, are by no means confined to anomalous metal distribution in water. Although the soft water—heart disease correlation has been confirmed in England, the US, Sweden and Finland, the opposite correlation appears to exist in Scotland. This Scottish correlation is in fact bogus for, on the full spectrum of the softness–hardness scale, both the major Scottish conurbations, Glasgow and Edinburgh, have soft water. Although the difference in acidity of their water supplies is too small to be reflected in disease statistics the fact that major differences in the incidence of heart disease actually exist may well mean that some other local factor, possibly metal contamination, is at work.

It happens that, in spite of the body's curiously efficient ability to concentrate in the kidney any cadmium that is absorbed, the rate of absorption from food and water is extremely slow. Something like 98% of the cadmium we eat or drink is in fact excreted in the normal way within 48 hours. Not only does this mean that differences of a few parts per billion in the cadmium content of drinking water will result in only marginal (although still possibly significant) differences in bodily uptake, but that such differences could easily be obscured by the cadmium content of foods whose distribution is not regional. The correlation with water may be real but it seems unlikely to show up clearly: meaningful results might only emerge from studies of *total* intake.

DOMINANT SOURCES

For if digestive absorption is slow the *absorption of cadmium from the air is very much faster*. Most mammals, including humans, absorb between 10% and 15% of inhaled cadmium when particles are small as in air pollution. This metal enters directly into the bloodstream, which means that we are physiologically much more sensitive to airborne cadmium contamination than to the low-level contamination of food and water. Thus the strongest correlations between heart disease and cadmium are likely to show most clearly in disease statistic comparisons of urban areas with cadmium-high and cadmium-low atmospheres. This is not to say that in many areas the intake of metals with the diet is of no significance, for all contributions are important. But if the air is contaminated to any significant extent then this is likely to be the dominant source, thus providing the least ambiguous basis for statistical analysis.

Curiously, in spite of the light such analyses might

throw on the incidence of heart disease, only one large survey appears to have been carried out. In 1965-6 a statistical analysis of 28 cities in the United States revealed a strong correlation between airborne cadmium and deaths from hypertension and heart disease.[6] The study was careful to examine the possibility of a general correlation with air pollution and found that none existed. The only other significant relationship appeared to be with zinc. Since zinc and cadmium occur together in nature and in industry it is not surprising that they should emerge together in a statistical study. There is, however, no evidence to implicate zinc as a cause of heart disease.

In spite of the unambiguous implication that cadmium is very probably the active agent, Dr Robert Nilsson, in his review of the toxicity of cadmium carried out for the Swedish Natural Science Research Council in 1970,[7] says that such correlations 'must be interpreted with the greatest caution,' an attitude which although scientifically proper must necessarily waver in the face of the increasing burden of evidence linking metals and diseases. There seems to be a tendency to lean over backwards in the search for other explanations rather than to investigate the obvious and synthesize findings which already point in one direction. For example, cadmium in tobacco leads to an increased cadmium intake by smokers. Smokers as a group suffer more frequently from hypertension than other population groups. Their kidney cadmium is also higher. These facts can be interpreted in two main ways. Either that people with hypertension tend to smoke more than other groups, in which case you can argue that the accumulation of cadmium in their kidneys is a secondary effect. Or you can argue that one outcome of smoking is hypertension as a result of the increased cadmium intake. Curiously the first argument seems to have dominated medical thinking during the 'sixties. Yet the second is more probable.

Analyses of humans who die from hypertensive effects (such as brain haemorrhage) show, according to Nilsson, that their kidney cadmium accumulations are significantly higher than those of non-hypertensive subjects. These are statistics which have to be carefully scrutinized to eliminate differences resulting from age, sex and living conditions, yet the implication is clear. When added to another correlation found by Prof. Schroeder, that of high milk cadmium levels and heart disease, the overall case against cadmium seems very strong, and it is not surprising that he is prepared to write dogmatically that 'there is little doubt ... that cadmium pollution is a major factor in human high blood pressure, from which 23 million Americans suffer.'[8] To these you might reasonably add some 25 million Europeans and other millions living in advanced industrial environments.

This is not to say that all hypertension is caused by cadmium, but that a significant proportion seems likely to be caused by the metal. Neither the extent of cadmium contamination, nor its full implication in cardiac disease can possibly be known until far more thorough studies are embarked upon and completed. Even then, because of the complexity of the contamination picture—involving a whole range of biologically potent pollutants whose interaction patterns are poorly understood—and the complexity of biological mechanisms, it will always prove impossible to be absolutely certain that in any single instance exposure to a specific metal has been a prime cause of a widespread type of disorder. The case can only be built up statistically and the question that the public health authorities have to answer is whether it seems probable that exposure to low levels of cadmium contamination involves significant health hazards. If the answer is yes—and I believe that there is enough evidence now to reach that answer—there should be no hesitation in imposing controls which are at the limit of practical stringency.

It is easy in the cadmium context to be deceived by the argument that, in industrial situations where cadmium exposure is often ten or even fifty times that experienced by the public in cadmium-rich areas, health investigations of workers fail to reveal evidence of hypertension. This is irrelevant. On the basis of other experimental evidence you would not expect such groups to suffer hypertension. But you would expect that effect among members of the general population experiencing much lower exposure to the metal. What proportion of the population this comprises and whether synergistic action with other metals is involved may never be completely determined. The need now is for action, not for long-winded discussion.

The curious biochemical quirk which results in hypertension from very low exposures to cadmium does not mean, however, that those who suffer larger exposures escape adverse effects. Far from it. The range of afflictions stemming from long and severe chronic exposure is both wide and bizarre. For instance, in 1955, the world learned of a new and appalling affliction which the Japanese called Itai-Itai-Byō. The name mimics the cries of sufferers and has been humourously translated as 'Ouchi-ouchi disease.' There is nothing humorous about it.

Endemic in a small area near Toyama City in northern Japan (but occasionally the direct outcome of industrial exposure), Ouchi-ouchi disease was first described at the 17th meeting of the Japanese Association of Orthopaedic Surgeons. Characteristically the disease takes a long course of increasing painfulness which, beginning with simple symptoms such as 'lumbago' or 'joint pains' ends with total and agonized immobility as the result of skeletal collapse. Cadmium leads to bone porosity and to the total inhibition of bone repair mechanisms so that, stage by stage as the disease progresses, the load-bearing bones of the skeleton suffer deformation, fracture and collapse. The agony accompanying such a process defies description and perhaps it suffices to say that, long before death, sufferers become confined to bed and 'characteristically reveal a decreased stature.' Once established, the disease is sometimes irreversible and death eventually follows from one or many associated causes.

In Japan incidence until recently appears to have been almost entirely among middle-aged women in an area which is metal-rich both from mining and zinc smelting, and in which agricultural land has become seriously contaminated by flooding which in the past has led to direct leakage from industrial cadmium-rich settling ponds. It is assumed that the disease has been prevalent in this one area for many years and, according to Dr Nilsson, over 200 cases were reported between 1962 and 1968. Although no attempt seems to have been made to calculate the extent of chronic exposure of those who suffer, the disease has been associated with high cadmium content of rice and soya (in the range 0·37 to 3·36 ppm dry weight) in the local diet. Lead and zinc were also very high but, remembering the 9·9 ppm cadmium recently discovered in grass in industrial Wales, these figures seem very low. It could well be that intake from water and from the atmosphere are both high, and that other dietary factors predispose some individuals towards the development of skeletal porosity. There is no doubt that cadmium is a prime cause, for the disease is known among cadmium workers and, in Japan, particularly among women engaged in the preparation of cadmium-based paints.

UNDERESTIMATED EFFECTS

With the blindness which seems to characterize the early industrial use of new materials, the toxicity of cadmium was grossly underestimated in the early years and chronic effects emerged only slowly. Many personal tragedies preceded tighter industrial control. Because of cadmium's extraordinary facility for accumulation in the kidney it is associated with kidney damage, but it also leads to cirrhosis of the liver, and severe damage to the lungs. Changes in cell structure and the development of fibrous tissue is typical, and animal experiments have confirmed that cadmium has cancer-inducing properties. As with lead, anaemia is an early symptom, and although the maximum allowable concentration for cadmium in industrial environments is set by many countries (including the US, West Germany and Sweden) at 100 micrograms per cubic metre, there is hard evidence that regular exposure to such levels is dangerous.[9] In animal experiments the metal has been shown to have powerful teratogenic effects which, typically, lead to malformations of the central nervous system. Higher doses lead to foetal death. In most mammals cadmium salts have been shown to result in irreversible destruction of testicular function and, since the rhesus monkey is among the animals shown experimentally to be sensitive, it seems that similar effects might be expected in man.

Most of these effects have been induced by cadmium exposures which far exceed those encountered by man except in industrial environments and then perhaps only through accident or oversight. Yet the high incidence of lung disorders among Swedish employees in a factory making nickel-cadmium accumulators, among workers in many countries engaged in smelting and alloying, and the long time-lag which can occur between exposure and the development of obvious damage both to the lungs and kidneys, suggests that present assessment of toxic levels may be completely erroneous. To what extent cadmium is involved in the development of chronic bronchitis in the general population, with which it must be associated since the metal produces pulmonary emphysema at low industrial exposure levels, can only be guessed.

Since abnormal growth rate and function of a number of organs, including the spleen and the heart, are implicit from animal experiments and have—certainly in the case of the heart—been to some extent confirmed at comparatively low levels of human exposure, it can be seen that cadmium fully justifies the label of 'possessing more lethal possibilities than any other metal.' In his collation of the literature on cadmium toxicology[7] Dr Nilsson lists some of these possibilities and extrapolates animal findings to give some indication of the exposure levels at which they might occur in humans. Most of these effects are relatively short-term, that is to say become manifest after 1 to 3 years exposure.

Pathological effect	Daily intake at which effect might be expected (in Micrograms):
Hypertension	175
Anaemia	530–50
Retardation of growth	1300
Abnormalities of spleen and pancreas	1300
Heart abnormalities	2125
Overt liver and kidney damage	5250

General effects, such as reduction of life-span, must be included at the lowest end of the scale, and when the intake is predominantly via the lungs, pulmonary damage probably slots in at the 500–900 microgram level. But even these figures which, at their lower end, confirm the likelihood of a correlation between cadmium and hypertensive disorders in the general population, fail to take into account the long-term effects of cadmium deposited in body tissues. Cadmium possesses, for example, a remarkable ability to decouple the enzymic processes of the liver and kidney so that stages in natural de-toxifying processes cease to function. Quite apart from its uniquely long residence time in the body, it appears to exert potentially damaging effects wherever it turns up in biochemical systems.

On the available evidence there is no effective treatment for many of the effects of cadmium poisoning and the inescapable conclusion is that the only sane course is to prevent exposure. Nilsson says bleakly that in those cases where cadmium poisoning has led to kidney damage

the prognosis is poor. Disablement and death have occurred in several cases. There seems to be no significant improvement in cases of apparent liver damage even after patients have been long removed from their contaminated surroundings. In certain cases the condition has actually deteriorated.

Much the same can be said of lung and heart conditions. Even more disturbing, in the context of organ damage, is the unfortunate characteristic of cadmium to produce highly toxic complexes with some of the common chelating agents. This means that attempts to mobilize damaging cadmium deposits so that they can be excreted are likely to result in damage that is even more severe than would be caused by the cadmium itself. No attempts appear to have been made to treat human cadmium poisoning with zinc-based chelating agents, although these might provide a partial escape from the toxic trap. The biochemical relationship between the metals has hardly been investigated.

But if the conditions induced by chronic industrial exposure are largely irreversible, the same is not necessarily true for the hypertensive effects resulting from much lower exposures. Over a long period the reduction of cadmium intake leads to a general reduction of levels in the bloodstream and, although kidney accumulations necessarily involve the risk of kidney damage, the firm bonding of cadmium to kidney and liver tissues means that the natural mobilization of accumulations is slow. Blood levels therefore tend to be a direct response to current levels of intake. If sources of cadmium can be eliminated or at least markedly reduced, then the benefits would accrue at all age levels. In time, perhaps a long time, they would accrue throughout all biological systems. The question, of course, is whether population exposures —as indicated by existing food and air concentrations of cadmium—seem likely to approach the 100–200 micrograms a day apparently necessary for the induction of hypertension.

Although the dispersion of cadmium in food chains is poorly monitored, and concentrations in normal diets must necessarily be approximations, Prof. H. A. Schroeder has estimated[10] that the daily intake in industrialized countries lies in the range 200–400 micrograms. Between 1% and 2% appears to be retained. A more recent German study based on 'shopping basket' type analyses,[11] suggests a lower daily intake, in the region of 100–300 micrograms. Neither of these estimates include absorption through the lungs but they suggest, very strongly, that there is *little room for additional intake without the immediate possibility of hypertensive effects*.

Taking the daily dietary intake to be 200 micrograms, between 2 and 4 micrograms enter the bloodstream and are eventually deposited in kidney and other tissues. Remembering the much higher efficiency of absorption through the lung, an atmospheric concentration of only 1 microgram per metre^3 would result in a doubling of the amount entering the bloodstream. This is a level of contamination which might easily be encountered in the vicinity of industrial plants whose processes involve the handling of large amounts of cadmium and which, if the moss-indicator studies in South Wales are typical of industrialized regions, may be widely prevalent.

PROBLEMS OF SCATTER

One of the disturbing features of the food is that concentrations of cadmium differ widely in even similar products, and that high concentrations are not always obviously explained. From normal soil concentrations of cadmium and the low level of cadmium uptake by plants, you would expect cereals to contain less than 0·1 ppm cadmium. In general, American samples were only a little above this level in the Schroeder survey, but *processed* cereals were very much higher at 0·3–0·5 ppm. In the same survey meat and chicken concentrations were inexplicably high, while kidney and liver concentrations—which you would expect to be universally high—had an enormous range of scatter, from less than 1·0 ppm to over 40·0 ppm. Within the range 0·05–6·0 ppm, a similar scatter was revealed among seafoods. It seems clear from this that without the detailed monitoring of many individual diets over a considerable period, no average assessment can be meaningful.

It is equally clear that contamination of food supplies and possibly food chains by cadmium has already reached serious levels. The scatter of concentrations in American seafood, like the differences in shellfish cadmium concentrations around British coasts, probably reflects local variations in levels of pollution. Where high concentrations are found in cereals, however, it seems much more likely that variations in natural soil content—probably aided and abetted by enrichment from fertilizers which sometimes have a surprisingly high cadmium content—may be to blame. But the characteristically high levels in processed cereals suggest contamination during processing. Like the higher cadmium contents of canned rather than fresh food as revealed by the two surveys, these high levels reflect a man-induced intensification of a naturally occurring problem, implying that the whole context of food production needs careful scrutiny. As in the case of mercury, it has been shown that cadmium used in fruit tree spraying translocates from the foliage to accumulate in the maturing fruit.[12] From the extreme examples of horse and cattle poisoning in Britain, it seems very likely that agricultural regions around large industrialized areas will inevitably produce cadmium-rich milk, meat and plant products.

From scanty food studies alone there seems to be a real and potentially dangerous cadmium problem in every advanced country—a problem in need of urgent study because of the paucity of present information and because of the explosive increase in cadmium use. It seems extraordinary that, after a series of acute poisoning incidents in the early years of cadmium plating, cadmium should be utterly banned from food trays and utensils but not even monitored in food. It is no less extraordinary that, although its extreme toxicity to marine and freshwater organisms is well known (the lethal level for daphnia is around 2·0 parts per *billion*), there have been no studies of concentration mechanisms in food chains and none of sedimentary accumulation. While, from the point of view of industrial hygiene it might be argued that the cadmium issue is under reasonable scrutiny, the effects of cadmium contamination on public health, and such problems as the fate of cadmium once it is in the environment, have been grossly neglected.

Even industrial control, when viewed internationally, appears to have been incredibly patchy in view of the wealth of evidence of chronic cadmium injuries. True, in 1956 and therefore within a year of the Japanese identification of Itai-Itai-Byō, chronic cadmium poisoning was added to the list of diseases prescribed under the British National Insurance (Industrial Injuries) Act. Yet the industrial evidence of cadmium induced diseases was strong in 1946 and it might reasonably be asked what had caused the delay. Since the prescription itself is an indication of the need to collect reliable data on the relationship between cadmium exposure and disease, the further delay of 11 years before chronic cadmium diseases became notifiable seems inexcusable. The kindest interpretation is that because the effects of cadmium exposure are often long-delayed the authorities were genuinely unaware of the toxicity of the metal. But if this is the case then it reveals a serious blindness in the protective system. Alternatively the delays may be regarded as yet more evidence of inertia caused by commitment both in industry and Government, to economically convenient views. Yet, in spite of these shortcomings, the British scene appears positively enlightened when compared to some others.

Japan, for example, which of all countries should have been most aware of cadmium dangers, seems to have exhibited extraordinary irresponsibility. Although working environments have been nominally under strict control since the 'forties, cadmium injuries appear to have been prevalent but largely unrecognized for 30 years. In 1971 at the height of the Japanese pollution controversy, the suicide of a former cadmium worker became, at last, the dramatic focus of a declared political change of heart. The suicide, a woman of 28, was the result of unbearable Itai-itai pain resulting from cadmium exposure *8 years earlier*.[13] A tightening up of industrial controls and a basic health scrutiny of workers in the 1000 or so industrial plants producing or using cadmium in Japan was ordered in February 1971. This was 2 years after the conscience-precipitating suicide, 10 years after the demonstration of severe dangers in the paint industry, 16 years after the identification of Itai-Itai-Byō and 31 years after the first serious warnings of danger from industrial hygienists.

CADMIUM EVERYWHERE

In Japan, and to a lesser extent in other industrialized countries, the regulatory and emission control systems have been apparently unable to cope with the explosive increase of cadmium use. Japan's '1000 plants or so' appears to be the only available estimate of the extent of cadmium use in any country, and although it is probably near the truth for Britain, West Germany and France, the figure may be very much larger in the US. While the sources of cadmium emission outside the zinc smelting, cadmium producing and alloying industries may be relatively small, they are extremely numerous. Cadmium is used in significant quantities in vehicle engine bearings, for example, and this use is reflected in higher than expected cadmium aerosol fallout near roads. Cadmium turns up in galvanized materials, in plastic, copper and galvanized piping, in almost every kind of wood finish, such as varnish, and in a massive and increasing number of paints. It lies beneath many chromium-plated surfaces as a rust preventing substrate, is a common constituent of hard solders, has a wide use in the protective coatings of marine metal fittings and comes into your home in food and maybe with the water.

The proliferation of use has certainly resulted in difficulties for control authorities but it can be seen that, even if it is assumed that industrial control of emissions is rapidly improved, background levels of cadmium could still be high in industrialized countries. Although the first look at water supplies in Britain suggested that cadmium contamination was rare, both river and tap water contamination appeared to be disturbingly common in the US when examined by Professor Schroeder in the mid-'sixties. Although limited to a relatively small area in the north-eastern region, municipal water in White Plains NY, Bridgeport, Connecticut and Brattleboro, Vermont, was found to contain cadmium at levels above the WHO and US Public Health Standards.[14] (See also note 10.) Characteristically, cold water that had been standing in pipes over-night was found to be highly contaminated (77 micrograms per litre, which is almost 8 times the permitted limit of 10 micrograms per litre) and hot water concentrations were in general higher than those of cold.

These findings are based on a small survey but they can only be interpreted as meaning that contamination may be more widespread than has hitherto been believed. Although this investigation suggested indirect routes of contamination, when added to the US survey of city atmospheres (and the discoveries of inexplicably high cadmium and other metal contamination in South Wales and the Severn estuary in Britain), it offers convincing evidence of both the need to look further and to apply new controls. Living things have evolved in an environment in which cadmium exists in association with zinc in a ratio of about 1:450. This relationship changes dramatically because of the inability of mammals to excrete cadmium once it has been absorbed. In the tissues of adult humans in the Western world the ratio, on average, is about 1:70, while in the kidneys of mammals including humans the ratio is around 1:1, revealing a concentration factor of about 500. It might well be that the ability of the mammalian kidney to bind cadmium is itself an evolved protective process, but even the presence of low concentrations of cadmium in the kidney and liver result in the decoupling of detoxification processes essential to the handling of other potentially poisonous materials. The tolerance limits, of both local structural damage to the organs and of interference with biochemical function, are extremely narrow, and there is no doubt whatever of cadmium's potency in disrupting enzyme systems.

It can be inferred that, if the body has a defensive capability, then its range of operation is highly limited and may not even cover the full extent of variation resulting from the natural geographical distribution of cadmium. Still less is it capable of handling the build-up of the metal resulting from chronic exposure to industrial contamination even when levels are low and regardless of the technological route. To permit the continued proliferation of cadmium use without the imposition of strict interim controls giving time for the contamination situation and its public health implications to be properly and responsibly assessed, is yet another example of the biological blindness and irresponsibility of technocracy.

FINELY DIVIDED NICKEL

While it seems certain that, like lead, cadmium is already producing deleterious effects on the health of the general public, the case against nickel is much more tentative. Although recognized as a hazard in the metal producing industries, and controlled as an effluent by river authorities in much the same way as other inorganic toxic materials, the possibility of airborne nickel contamination is not entertained seriously by public health authorities in the Western world. As far as can be seen there have been no official investigations of urban atmospheres for nickel, and no attempts to evaluate possible routes for the production of nickel-based compounds in the environment or in existing gaseous effluent systems. Nickel, like mercury, is a common constituent of all fossil fuels, and although like lead it may well be thought to precipitate out in stacks, there is at least one potential route of escape which needs investigation. It is very relevant that a profile of high nickel contamination has been uncovered by the Swansea University studies of South Wales, for in that region lies an industrial plant employing the remarkable process involving the nickel carbonyl deposition technique evolved last century by Dr Ludwig Mond.

The unmasking of the carbonyls, in which metals can exist in a gaseous form at room tenperature, was a classic scientific discovery that rested, typically, on a combination of acute observation and accident. It was found that, if carbon monoxide was passed over finely divided nickel at low temperatures (typically around 80°C) a gaseous compound was formed which, at higher temperatures (above 180°C) decomposed back into the metal and free carbon monoxide. Although nickel carbonyl has several forms the basic equation looks like this: $Ni + 4 CO \rightleftharpoons Ni (CO)_4$. The discovery of this unexpected compound was made through the accidental use of nickel fittings in a chemical plant, and the subsequent examination of their curious encrustations in the laboratory. The formation and subsequent decomposition of the carbonyl provides a route for the preparation of extremely pure nickel from highly impure starting material. (The temperatures of the forward and reverse processes are well separated and are specific to individual metals.) Thus Dr Mond and his associates at Brunner-Mond (now ICI) were able to develop an elegantly engineered automatic process for the production of highly pure nickel that, 80 years later, is still regarded as a model of chemical engineering skill.

The need for a totally enclosed system was enforced from the outset by the toxicity of the working fluid, carbon monoxide, and by the simple need for economic operation. But early technical failures at the plant led to the occasional exposure of workmen to the circulating gas and within a decade of starting operations it became clear that nickel carbonyl was considerably more toxic than the carbon monoxide from which it was built.

Now carbon monoxide is poisonous because it is transported across lung membrane, and by haemoglobin, as if it were oxygen, but instead of meeting the biochemical demand for oxygen when it is distributed by the bloodstream it simply blocks the oxygen-using pathways. It turned out that, in the case of nickel carbonyl, the carbon monoxide component of the molecule was readily broken off and transported across the lung membrane to produce typical carbon monoxide poisoning. Although rapidly fatal at high exposures, this is completely reversible when exposures are low and normally provides no great source of worry about chronic effects. But at the lung membrane itself the nickel of the nickel carbonyl molecule is deposited in a very finely divided state over the whole of the lung's elegantly massive internal surface. It constitutes a nickel recovery system that is far more efficient than anything that can be achieved by industry!

The direct toxicity of nickel carbonyl is now taken to be 5 to 10 times that of carbon monoxide,[15] a point of great importance in industrial hygiene. But public health considerations involve, not direct toxicity, but the long-term effects of this highly efficient deposition of nickel in the lung. For it seems chemically possible that the production of nickel carbonyl is by no means confined to the handful of industrial plants in which it is exploited commercially. All that is required chemically is the existence of nickel in a carbon monoxide rich atmosphere at the right reaction temperature. And nickel is a highly active cancer causing agent.

Nickel is contained in amounts varying from a few parts per billion up to several parts per million in fossil fuels, such as coal, diesel oil and other petroleum products. One estimate indicates that, on a global basis, about 70,000 tons of nickel reach the atmosphere each year from these sources. This is the equivalent of one sixth of the total production of the metal and on 1971 prices is worth about £45 million ($120 million), a figure which suggests that recovery would at least partially pay for its own costs. But the point is that this surprisingly large amount of nickel reaches the atmosphere through industrial and domestic stacks, and through the exhaust systems of vehicles, which provide both a temperature gradient and a carbon monoxide rich atmosphere. While at the hot end of all these systems the temperatures are likely to be well above the decomposition point of nickel carbonyl, there will necessarily be a progression of the gas mixture through an area in which the carbonyl can be produced and transported stably into lower temperature areas and finally into the atmosphere. In practice (since no one seems to have done the elementary monitoring to demonstrate otherwise), this may well be happening and, although the process is of low efficiency even when conditions are optimal, an unknown quantity of nickel carbonyl seems likely to be contaminating the atmosphere. The 'hot spots' would be industrial and urban complexes and the question is whether—if concentrations occur—the resultant deposition of nickel on the linings of lungs is of significance in disease patterns.

Nickel is accepted as being responsible for lung cancer and other lung diseases among workers and, although there is little at the moment to suggest that nickel contamination is a particularly virulent component of either food or air pollution, its efficiency as an agent of cellular damage could be dramatically increased when in a finely divided state on the surface of lung tissue. If enhanced potency does occur then even a very small nickel carbonyl component in urban air could be of significance—a point which has been made by Prof. H. A. Schroeder.

Those general studies that have been made of the distribution of nickel in the environment and in man,[16] while acknowledging the possibility that in very small amounts nickel salts might be an essential micro-nutrient in mammals, indicate that a great deal remains to be learned. We must know more about the way nickel works as metal in the cell, its local effect when accumulated on the surface of lung tissue and the biochemical pathways along which it travels during detoxification processes. The presence of nickel carbonyl in the atmosphere must necessarily carry an element of risk, although at the moment no reliable estimate of the extent of risk can be made. This strikes me as being an instance in which only a little expenditure is needed to establish whether the risk is real or notional. If it turns out to be real there are relatively simple ways of ensuring the breakdown of nickel carbonyls in stacks and of recovering high purity nickel. Even if calculated on the customary one-eyed 'cost to industry' basis, recovery of nickel might prove worthwhile. If not, then weighed as preventative medicine, the savings in social costs might tip the balance far enough to satisfy the economic hawks. Yet the immediately essential steps, those of determining whether nickel carbonyl is produced accidentally in significant quantities, and whether urban 'hot spots' exist, seem unlikely to be taken seriously by the authorities in either the US or Britain. While scientific and public pressures have forced some official attention onto the problems posed by lead, mercury and cadmium, the potential problems of nickel remain in the shadow.

It might be argued that, with so many compounds of unknown potency entering the atmosphere and the water and food cycles, it is impossible to monitor them all: but in this instance specific possibilities can be proposed and their validity checked out fairly simply. Since apparently extensive nickel contamination has been demonstrated in a more or less typical British urban-industrial complex, a little imagination and an early investigatory programme would be no more than prudent insurance for those whose business is to ensure public protection.

BLINKERED THINKING

Reactionary pressures, however, such as the commercial impetus behind lead pollution or the cheapness and convenience of dumping toxic wastes in the sea rather than attempting to treat and recycle them, continue to demand that actual damage must be demonstrated before any case for a change of policy will be entertained. Only when rivers are dead, estuaries dying and inland seas grievously injured, do authorities begin to move. Inevitably, because medical authorities are concerned with public health, the threat of human injury tends to move them into action more rapidly than any environmental threat. Indeed, the medical authorities are the most powerful of our protectors, but their present approach has grave weaknesses. Because their view is centred entirely on man, it totally ignores the most serious aspects of local and global contamination, the continuing and increasing disruption of natural systems on which all life depends.

One example of disastrously blinkered thinking of this kind, and examples are depressingly frequent, cropped up in the *British Medical Journal* in June when, as an afterthought to the emergence of marine mercury problems, this august journal dismissed virtually all human health hazards from metallic or pesticide contamination as myths. 'Nature pours more mercury into the oceans than man,' it said erroneously, 'and dentists put more mercury into our teeth each year than farmers apply as fungicides.'[17] In the face of extensive and proven freshwater and marine contamination of a most serious nature, such obtuseness seems deliberate. Even a minimal passing knowledge of the complexity and extent of the metallic contamination problem would unmask the dangerous absurdity of such a comparison, and the only conclusion is that minimal knowledge was not applied. 'The final evidence that pesticide residues are not a health hazard stems mainly from what were called "market basket" samples . . .' says the article. 'Certainly traces of persistent materials like DDT can be found, but this is present in no greater amounts than the even more persistent arsenic.'[18]

Arsenic may have been a deliberate choice, for it is of relatively low toxicity and may be an essential micronutrient, but the argument is so narrowly based that it misses all the most important issues. By far the most serious worry about persistent pesticides is not their effects on humans, but their incredibly powerful lethal effects on essential organisms in living systems. They are, by design, less toxic to higher mammals than to virtually every other kind of living thing, and some essential food chain organisms are so sensitive that the presence of only a few parts per billion of an organochlorine compound is disruptive or even fatal. The medical argument ignores potentiating effects, such as that between pesticides,[19] and the synergistic effects of contaminants with similar properties. Mercury, lead and the organochlorines all affect the central nervous system, for example, and to consider them in isolation even in assessing human health risks, is to court disaster. But, and this perhaps is the main point, the examination and evaluation of human health risks as if these were in some magical way disconnected from their ecological context is to ignore the whole interactive biological basis of life. Human beings are extraordinarily complex and resilient organisms much less vulnerable to some poisons than the different, but no less complex, creatures of other ecological niches, functions and environments. If you do not believe that, try putting your gin and tonic in the fish tank!

This is not to suggest that the effects of metals or organochlorines in human tissue are not a proper subject for the evaluation of medical risks, but that to dismiss risks on a blinkered human basis and in a falsely narrowed context is grossly misleading, even though it may seem medically justifiable. Since the medical authorities provide the most powerful protective structure, both in the sense of public voice and of publicly undiscussed policy formulation, their restricted viewpoint can result in yawning gaps in essential defences.

Even when considering human whole-population effects there appears, in practice, a need to demonstrate overt damage by a specific contaminant, before elimination beyond that which is cost-minimal (at the polluter's end) can be justified on health grounds. This leads to the disappearance of pro-protective arguments in a veritable medical quagmire. Metals, as we have seen, are particularly potent because their biological effects stem from direct interference with essential enzyme systems. In general, enzyme levels are measured in the bloodstream, not necessarily at the site of action, and not only are there considerable variations between individuals in enzyme levels which can be considered 'normal,' but there is conclusive evidence that for many enzyme functions a natural reserve of essential enzymes exists within the biological system. There is, as it were, a kind of natural buffer capable of absorbing the enzyme changes induced by small amounts of toxic materials.

From the existence of this normally redundant reserve buffer of enzymes (or co-enzymes or any components of the enzyme production chain) it can be inferred that the functions of a biological system, human or otherwise, can tolerate small doses of toxic materials without suffering damage. This is one important facet of the medical notion of 'threshold' levels below which no damage will occur. Another facet, in the case of transient exposure to toxic materials, is that the living cell contains repair mechanisms which are capable of restoring chemical functions that have suffered only limited damage. In the continuing argument about background radiation, for example, the function of repair mechanisms plays a crucial role. This is because at low levels of exposure (even at double those encountered from natural sources, the magic line agreed as 'acceptable' by nuclear protective agencies without public consultation) most of the damage is made good by cellular systems.

There is, however, very strong evidence that at any level of exposure a proportion of the damage will be of a kind which, although not fatal to the cell, will be beyond the repair capability of natural mechanisms. If this residual damage is in genetic material then one facet of it will show up as an increased incidence of specific diseases, such as leukaemia. The Sternglass–Gofman–Tamplin controversy about the whole-population effects of small radiation doses, which rocked the US in the late 'sixties and which—in spite of fully justified scientific criticism of the arguments of Professor Sternglass—is far from being resolved, rests on the interpretation of the effects of residual damage. It needs to be remembered that radiation damage usually kills a cell, and that the marginal proportion of cells which remain viable but damaged is the same at all radiation levels. There exists no demonstrated threshold below which no residual damage remains. The same appears to be true of those metals which have mutagenic properties.

TOXIC INSULTS

Some idea of the toxic insult suffered by cells at low concentrations of metal salts or other complexes can be gathered from the number of metallic molecules likely to be present in a cell if the concentration is that specified as an 'allowable concentration' in drinking water. While it certainly does not follow that, if metals occur at this concentration in drinking water they will permeate cellular systems in a uniform way, permeation certainly occurs. The molecular numbers are large and we can only speculate at what threshold, if any, the normal cell will become impaired or suffer mutation under insult.[20]

However, although mercury is one of the most powerful of known mutagens, and nickel possesses marked mutagenic properties, the main activity of most metals is that of blocking enzyme systems. Lead, for example, causes anaemia. It does so because it interferes with haem synthesis by inhibiting the activity of the essential enzyme delta-aminolevulinic acid dehydrase (ALA dehydrase for short). As can be seen in FIG. 5:2, there is no threshold level below which lead has no effect.

WHO allowable concentration Milligrams per litre (ppm)		Molecular insult to cell at WHO concentration
Arsenic	0·05	100,000
Cadmium	0·01	12,500
Chromium-6	0·05	145,000
Cyanide	0·20	1,150,000
Lead	0·05	36,000
Selenium	0·01	19,000

Here, then, is a firm indication that the notion of a 'threshold level' below which toxic action does not occur, is entirely illusory. Does this necessarily mean that real damage is being done? In this particular instance it has been argued that the critical correlation between ALA dehydrase blood level and the onset of anaemia varies widely, and that overt biochemical interference with the enzyme would be demonstrated by the excretion of large amounts of ALA dehydrase building block—ALA itself. Excretion does not rise to significant levels until the activity of the enzyme has been reduced to about one tenth of 'normal,' a level of inhibition associated with industrial rather than urban exposure to lead. For those arguing that a little lead does you no harm, this is a plausible argument, and in the case of a contaminant that is universal and cannot therefore be easily assessed statistically since there exist no lead-free control groups, is difficult to refute.

Yet the universal presence in the population of a contaminant which depresses an enzyme directly concerned with a vital function, such as haem synthesis, *must have an effect on public health*. There is no sharp division between 'well' and 'unwell' even in its most general interpretation, and in the case of specific disorders related to enzyme function the distribution of 'well' and 'unwell' in the population forms a curve around 'normal' like that

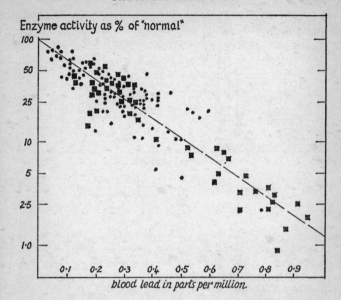

FIG. 5.2. Inhibition of the activity of a blood enzyme by lead. Notice that the vertical scale is logarithmic. At only 0·2 ppm of lead in the blood (below the present city norm) enzyme activity is reduced to only 30%. The dots represent measurements of the blood values of students and printers, and the squares those of car mechanics and employees in lead smelters. This graph indicates that, in the case of one blood enzyme, there is no 'threshold' below which lead has no effect.

in FIG. 5:3. Because of variations between individuals there exists an area of uncertainty in which, although a measurement appears abnormal, it is not necessarily accompanied by a fall-off in functional efficiency.

But the presence of a *universal* contaminant, since it will affect the whole population, necessarily results in a shift of the position of the curve because all measurements will be affected in the same direction. Although you can pretend that the new 'normal' level is a genuine norm (even though in uncontaminated circumstances it would be different), the area of uncertainty must still occur at the

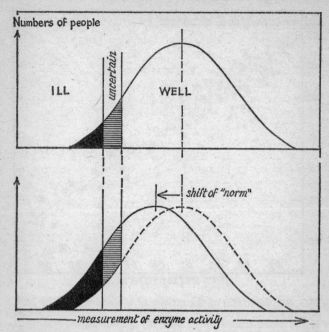

FIG. 5:3. Many levels of enzyme activity provide a measure of the state of health of an individual, although at the borderline between 'ill' and 'well' is an area of uncertainty in which some individuals—with naturally low enzyme activity—will be perfectly well, while others will be already ill. This area of doubt leads to difficulties when trying to decide whether small changes of enzyme activity caused by pollutants are of significance to public health. But a widespread contaminant, such as lead, results in a whole-population shift of the 'norm' of the population distribution curve. The result, as the diagram shows, is that a larger proportion of the population move into the 'ill' sector, and a larger proportion enters the 'uncertain' area. The 'gaussian' curve used here is typical of a population distribution of a medical measurement.

same blood-enzyme levels. This means that the shift of the curve carries an additional proportion of the population into both the 'unwell' and 'uncertain' categories.

This is precisely what shows up when morbidity or mortality statistics of different areas are compared as, for instance, in the US, with 28 city surveys looking for the effects of cadmium. But it can be seen that, when a contaminant is *universally* present—as in the case of lead—this kind of difference does not exist and therefore cannot show up. Further, those comparative studies which might reveal the public health effects, such as a comparison of urban and rural populations, involve so many differing factors that single effects, such as that of lead, become obscured by the statistical 'noise.' *It is not that effects do not exist, but that they cannot be unambiguously demonstrated to exist*, a practical fact which in the case of lead has nourished the argument for inactivity on the part of control agencies for 20 years. It is likely to be employed in the obfuscation of any attempt to persuade authorities to tighten controls of many other widely dispersed contaminants.

Yet since any large local population, whether of a city or a region, will display a distribution curve of the FIG. 5:3 type for any health parameter you care to measure, and since the presence of an enzyme disturbing contaminant will result in the tipping of an unknown proportion of the population into the 'unwell' area, the argument that this cannot be demonstrated in practice is really not an argument at all. It has been clearly demonstrated, as was indicated in Chapter 3, that undefinable illness among the adult population can be cured by chelation therapy. To pretend that the group which responded to treatment, consisting of the elimination of metallic contaminants, were in some way special would be pushing probability much too far. It seems very likely that they were simply representative of that unrecognized proportion of the population which has been tipped over the brink into ill health by ubiquitous contaminants.

Again, when weighing the notion of 'threshold' levels of poisons, the question of locality of damage through organ selection needs to be borne in mind. Although the ability of mercury to damage selectively the nervous system and particular areas of the brain has an obscure and at the moment wholly mysterious biochemical basis. (There is no doubt that—as in the case of radiation damage —sub-lethal cell damage is largely repaired in neural as in other tissues.) But at any level of exposure there will be some cell deaths and some residual damage in cells which survive. In neural tissues such damage is permanent and necessarily affects the viability of functions with advancing age. The accepted 'threshold' of clinical damage is that at which a diminution of function can be observed. As Dr Göran Löfroth has written:

> The question arises of whether these effects are brought about only at and above some threshold value of methyl-mercury intake. As to *gross* clinical symptoms one can state that a threshold mechanism is operating. This threshold mechanism is, however, not due to a methylmercury thres-hold but to a threshold in the number of damaged brain cells. After a damage of one or a few cells other cells may take over—the net result showing up as no effect in the clinical investigation. When too many cells have been dam-aged during a short time the clinical effects show up early. This kind of mechanism can, erroneously, be classified as a methylmercury threshold mechanism.
>
> Nothing is known about the methylmercury concentra-tion which can cause irreversible damage to single cells. However, even a low frequency of brain cell damage, above the natural inactivation rate of these cells, has during a long time an effect on the organism as the number of available cells for each function is limited. Such damage may have serious effects in the later stages of life.[21]

Similar considerations may reasonably be felt to apply to the accumulation of cadmium in the kidneys, although the problem is one of intensified insult rather than the inability of cells to replace themselves. But the clinical recognition of damage, in this and in any other instance of metallic insult, is necessarily based on overt symptoms. By the time these appear it is inevitable that extensive damage has already taken place.

It seems self-evident that in the case of any persistent

contaminants—and the metals are highly persistent when either in the environment or in the organism—it has to be assumed that they will cause damage once released into the environment. There is no question of them degrading into innocuous forms. On the contrary, in many instances they may well be converted into more toxic forms than those in which they are released. To argue that calculated risks are necessary for the survival of industries of one kind or another indicates not only a feeble acceptance of Western economic tyranny (and environmentally it remains precisely that in spite of one or two marginal ecological victories) but a rejection of ordinary common sense. It has already been more than adequately demonstrated that we need to be especially careful when dealing with persistent materials. Yet outside the factory walls the evidence of lack of care is proliferating. We ignore the evidence at our peril.

EPILOGUE

The extent to which economic pressures corrupt the statements of public health authorities is seldom fully clear. The fog provided by interpretive latitude and by selection of data is generally impenetrable without careful analysis. But, taking the case of cadmium it is reasonable to say that, once widespread in agricultural areas, it is costly to remove and quite impossible within the economics of agriculture itself. It is also fair to say that this is one of the metals against which the human body has no real protection. Japan, suffering the effects of extensive cadmium pollution and, armed with the knowledge of cadmium's appalling effects from earlier poisoning incidents, discovered during monitoring in 1970 that some agricultural areas were producing grain and greenfoods which contained almost 18·0 ppm cadmium. On Government advice cropping of some cereals and vegetables was curtailed. Public reaction against the authorities for permitting this state of affairs to develop was strong. According to *Time* magazine, in a speech early in 1971, Mr Masuo Araki, Chairman of the Japanese National Public Safety Commission, came up with a startling reassurance: 'The human body has functions to discharge foreign wastes', he said. 'We must have the spirit to consume contaminated rice.'[13]

References and Notes

1. F. C. Christensen and E. C. Olsen: 'Cadmium Poisoning.' *Archives of Industrial Health*, vol 16:8, 1957.

2. H. M. Perry and A. Yunice: Proceedings of the Society for Experimental Biology and Medicine, vol 120, 805, 1965.

3. H. A. Schroeder and W. A. Vinton: 'Hypertension Produced in Rats by Small Doses of Cadmium,' *American Journal of Physiology*, vol 202:515–18, March 1962.

4. H. A. Schroeder: 'Cadmium Hypertension in Rats,' *American Journal of Physiology*, vol 207:62–6, July 1964.

5. H. A. Schroeder: 'Action of a Chelate of Zinc on Trace Metals in Hypertensive Rats,' *American Journal of Physiology*, vol 214:796–800, April 1968.

6. R. E. Carroll: *Journal of the American Medical Assn*, vol 198:177, 1966.

7. R. Nilsson: 'Aspects of the toxicity of cadmium and its compounds,': Swedish Natural Science Research Council, Ecological Research Committee Bulletin No 7, March 1970.

8. H. A. Schroeder: 'Trace Elements in the Human Environment', *The Ecologist*, vol 1:11, May 1971.

9. K. Tsuchiya: *Archives of Environmental Health*, vol 14:875, 1967.

10. H. A. Schroeder and others: 'Essential Trace Metals in Man—Zinc. Relation to environmental Cadmium,' *Journal of Chronic Diseases*, vol 20:179–210, April 1967.

11. R. Kropf and others: *Archives of Hygiene and Bacteriology*, vol 152:218, 1968.

12. R. G. Ross and D. K. R. Stewart: *Canadian Journal of Plant Science*, vol 49:49, 1969.

13. This incident was reported in *Time* magazine, March 8 1971, p 34.

14. H. A. Schroeder: 'Municipal Drinking Water and Cardiovascular Death Rates,' *Journal of the American Medical Association*, vol 195:2, January 1966.

15. Report of the International Congress on Industrial Accidents and Occupational Diseases, Leipzig: vol 2:248, 1939. This assessment appears not to have been superseded.

16. H. A. Schroeder and others: 'Abnormal Trace Metals in Man—Nickel,' *Journal of Chronic Diseases*, vol 15:51–65, 1962.

17. 'Pesticides and Priorities,' leading article, *British Medical Journal*, vol 2:5761, June 5 1971.

18. See reference 17.

19. See for example W. B. Deichman and others: 'DDT Tissue Retention—sudden rise induced by Aldrin,' *Science*, vol 172:275–6, April 1971.

20. C. D. Reed and J. A. Tolley, 'Hazards from the kitchen tap,' *Journal of the Royal College of General Practitioners*, vol 21:289, 1971.

21. G. Löfroth: 'Methylmercury,' Swedish Natural Science Research Council: Ecological Research Committee Bulletin No 4, 1970, p 5.

CHAPTER SIX

HIGHWAYS TO DISASTER

Through the dubious assumption that industrial data can be applied safely to whole populations, public health authorities and industrial hygienists have condoned the growing contamination of urban and other environments with cadmium, lead and a host of other metals of great toxicity. This condonation has not been accompanied by an urgent sense of the need to monitor and to gather the statistical information necessary to test the initial assumption. In industrial hygiene the initial assumptions have—characteristically, when the major governing factor is economic—seriously underestimated the effects of chronic exposure on humans. There is every reason to fear that this is also the case for population exposures and for the contamination of the environment as a whole.

Medicine does not consider overall environmental effects. River authorities do not consider estuarial effects. Until very recently Government monitoring agencies have been concerned predominantly with toxic residues in human diets. Thus the fragmentation of departmental responsibility results in the avoidance of areas of overlap essential to the proper integration of control. When, under the pressure of public concern, authorities produce an index of the pollution status of the environment, the choice of presentation is often one which gives a falsely rosy picture. Typically, for example, the extent of Britain's freshwater contamination is expressed as 'miles of river', taking 'river' to mean virtually every water course down to small streams. On that basis 75% of rivers are 'unpolluted or recovering from pollution.'[1] But if this is assessed, as it should be, as a proportion of water flow then, since the majority of large rivers are seriously polluted, a very different picture would emerge.

Since no figures are available, either for Britain, other European countries or for the US, it is only possible to guess. But it seems quite probable that something like 60% to 70% of the water volume reaching the seas from industrial countries is seriously polluted. That is what matters: the 'miles of river' which comprise the feeder networks above the regions of serious pollution are irrelevant to the contamination problem but they make it *sound much less serious*. It is, to say the least, a matter of some concern that protection agencies—in Britain's case the river authorities—and the responsible Government departments should employ such deceptive tactics.

Further, it is very noticeable that the toxicities of metals (and other environmental contaminants) seem always to be considered singly, a hang-over from the laboratory necessity to produce unambiguous figures for lethality in experimental biological systems. Such an assessment has no relevance to the real environmental situation. *Contaminants never occur singly*, are often additive or even synergistic in their effects and present a gross insult of great complexity and perhaps of enormously enlarged potential for damage. While it is true that all living systems, through their ability to break down poisonous substances into reusable chemical building blocks, have great powers of detoxification *provided that the system does not become overloaded*, the toxic metals cannot be broken down in this way. They do not degrade: they are *never* rendered innocuous and, once in a natural cycle, they remain active until laid deeply into sediments. Their period of biological potency has, in some circumstances, to be measured in thousands of years.

The various graphs of metal production given in earlier chapters are, in effect, graphs of utilization. They indicate the growing masses of metallic material now being artificially mobilized and, ultimately, released by a host of different routes into the environment. Even in terms of resources conservation these are pointers of madness. Many of the non-renewable resources of metals (and other raw materials) are now being depleted at a rate which will ensure their exhaustion within the next half century, even if it is absurdly assumed that Third World consumption remains negligible.[2] The wilful insanity of blind technological 'expansion' with its phoney rosy futures, of seeking ever greater Gross National Products as if these were not a measure of resources destruction and of pretending that technological nostrums such as the 'green revolution' are really an answer to the exponential growth of population, has been starkly exposed by many writers of authority during the past decade. Yet economists and Governments appear to be universally blind to the obvious while individuals, if increasingly aware that all is far from well, are seemingly powerless and perhaps too committed to want—or to comprehend—the enormous changes implicit in the hard facts of planetary limitation.

It is therefore necessary to play for time, although the signs are that there is not a great deal of time to play with. In 1970-1, at the request of an informal group of industrialists and humanists who call themselves the Club of Rome and really care about the future, the management studies department of Massachusetts Institute of Technology took a startling look ahead. By feeding basic facts, trends and appropriate—if simple—mathematical models into a computer, it was discovered that on the best available evidence mankind has a choice between disaster and worse disaster.[3] The work is going ahead with better mathematical models but these initial findings were said to have come as a grave shock to Governments and their technological advisors. They will hardly surprise biologists and environmentalists who have been pointing out the reality of the human and environmental crises for a couple of generations.

One of the nubs of the crisis, revealed sharply by the MIT study, is the direct relationship between pollution protection and an increased drain on resources. The technological answer to technological problems is more technology which, necessarily means increased production of non-productive equipments. The result of attempting extreme conservation of resources while attempting to maintain existing 'quality of life' is predicted as a massive population–pollution explosion early next century, a cataclysmic population collapse, and a dramatic drop in the quality of conditions for the survivors. One MIT alternative, which gives priority to environment protection in spite of its demands on resources, while also attempting to maintain living standards, is a less dramatic population and pollution crisis at around the same time (2020), and a steady decline in living standards from 1970 onward.

It has been obvious for many years, and is increasingly obvious every day, that the overriding aim should be stability through birth-restraint, resources conservation and genuine control. Counsels of gloom implicit in the MIT study could promote inactivity for the predictions refer to crises already with us and apparently out of control. They suggest that however hard we try we cannot cure environmental degeneration, a situation all too easily exploitable as an excuse for doing nothing. On the contrary it should spur Governments to recognize the overriding case for ensuring that the complex basis of life on this planet remains as intact and as healthy as possible. In spite of human profligacy and blind greed, there may be survivors who need the support of planetary life systems. If they are lucky your grandchildren may even be among those survivors.

BEYOND THE GLOOM

In spite of the gloomy outlook it seems good sense to select now those contaminants likely to be of most serious consequence, and to treat them with appropriate diligence. Since the toxic metals comprise a most serious long-term threat they, like other persistent toxic materials, should be at the top of the list. Quite apart from the benefit stemming from minimizing interference with ecological structures, there is clearly a possibility of long-term gains from the recycling of essential materials. Industrialists and, in the main, economists in their myopic visions of rosy futures set great store by a gradual transition from a vectored economy (raw material—fabrication—consumption—garbage disposal) to a recycling economy (raw material—fabrication—consumption—recovery of raw material), and the trend towards the recovery of used material is certainly growing. It will grow faster in specific instances as resources of particular materials dwindle, costs rise and recovery becomes justifiable in 'economic' terms.

But once dispersed into the environment, into sea water for example in a few parts per thousand billion, energy requirements for recovery accelerate sharply and soon go well beyond the physical limits of the planet. It is not that the optimistically envisaged transition from nuclear to fusion power will not open up the road to unlimited energy resources, but that there exist strict limits to the amount of energy which can be generated on earth without seriously disrupting the overall thermal budget of the system. Indeed, if the 1970 population of the earth was to have the *per-capita* energy requirements of the average 1970 US citizen, then that limit would already be reached. There is, unfortunately, no way out of the energy problem. You cannot manipulate the laws of thermodynamics. This means, perhaps not this century but certainly early in the next, that the possibility of recovery will be sharply limited. We can stretch the time-scale of approach by careful conservation; we can pretend that 'substitutes' will be found and that these will require less energy (probably the reverse of the truth, as plastics indicate), and we can hope that population and raw material demands will eventually stabilize. But the planetary limits of resources and energy tolerance remain and will in the end determine the limits of possibility.

All this may seem some way from the consideration of toxic metals. But, because of their enormous value to industry, and because of the comparative rarity of many of them, the spiral of shortage, costs, increased energy demand and the foreseeably desperate political pressures stemming from conflict over Third World sources will strike us first through the toxic, rare, but invaluable materials like mercury, lead, vanadium, selenium, cadmium and copper.

So, quite apart from the issues of environmental disruption by trace amounts of metallic poisons, and the growing problems these pose to public health, there are sound long-term economic and resource reasons for reducing as far as possible their dispersal into the environment. It will be argued, especially by European and—in particular—British control agencies, that this is what they have been doing for many years. So they have, up to a point, although the pollution record of the Continent of Europe during the profligate period of post-World War II economic–industrial expansion has been grim.

Yet whenever a particular contaminant reveals itself as damaging it is always found that something can be done to improve the situation. For every reason we should insist that the situation is improved *before* the damage is done, because in many instances the barrier is not one of short-term economics (industry's greatest ally in perpetuating bad practices) but of damnably bad systems analysis and design of recovery systems. This was perhaps epitomized in the analysis of the mercury-cell chlor-alkali process carried out at Oak Ridge during the great US mercury scare. When the system losses of mercury were examined in detail (0·5 lb of mercury catalyst for every ton of chlorine produced) it was concluded that this could 'be decreased by one or two orders of magnitude by proper plant management.'[4] In other words, simply by *additional attention to the details of design for recovery and by careful operational control,*

*the discharge of mercury into the environment could be
reduced to one tenth, and perhaps one hundredth of the
amount accepted as normal by the industry*, and as permissible by control agencies.

There is nothing to be gained by exacerbating the
already heightened sense of conflict between industry and
social conscience, and everything to be gained from a
genuine integration of social, industrial, environmental
and economic aims. It needs only an adjustment of
attitudes, not an agonizing reappraisal of market and
profit motives, or a dramatic escalation of industrial
capital expenditure on protective procedures, to achieve
a very large reduction in contamination and considerable
conservation of resources. Yet, in spite of the growing
realization that this is true, and the increasingly large
sector of public opinion pressing for the abandonment
of purely economically orientated expansion,[5] change is
insolently and dangerously slow.

Since the combined economic effects and social modifications imposed by the twin ogres of *defence* and
international commercial operations now far exceed the
controlling powers of Governments, it might be argued
that change is unlikely and can occur in only a limited
sector of human activity. But the very fact that pressure
toward *socially* and *environmentally* oriented economies
is highest in those countries most seriously affected by expansionist industrial laissez-faire—Japan and the United
States—leads to the optimistic conclusion that the rejection of one-eyed economic policies has already begun, and
that the process might expand. It happens that, because
the United States has a far more open system of government than most other advanced nations, it is more easily
possible for US pressure groups to take the lid off environmental problems and to probe into the purposes and
motives of some aspects of government, industry and
defence. This leads not only to a much higher level of
awareness of environmental and social problems than is
common elsewhere (which spills over, incidentally, into

Canada), but to the forcing of dramatic gestures of apparent policy improvements at Federal level.

Sadly, the powers of such demonstrably vocal democracy are frustrated by the essentially democratic nature of legal principles and practice. The gesture of environmental control is hamstrung by the legal injunction. Legislation, however necessary and carefully formulated, can be effectively delayed indefinitely through recourse to the courts of law. That is why, in spite of attempts at control, something like 27,000 tons of DDT went onto North American soil in 1970. Further, because the sense of conflict between the Government and industry is heightened by recourse to law, other age-old techniques of conflict are employed. As in the dark days of the industrial revolution it appears necessary to legislate to protect the vulnerable labour force, whose livelihood becomes a pawn in the pressure game as industry reacts against the 'intolerable' costs of carrying out their operations with proper responsibility for the environment and for the future.[6]

In a situation of conflict, rather than co-operation in environmental control, it becomes necessary for power of law enforcement to be mandatory, rather than discretionary. In the US, for example, considerable latitude still exists for the application of water pollution control measures in spite of the existence of the Federal agency for Environmental Protection. Considerable discretionary powers exist at State level and with pollution control officers. The persuasive strength of local benefit from industrial investment and development, and of real estate development without adequate provision of sewage treatments, lead to considerable bending of apparently tight legislation.

In the more secretive systems of Europe, the situation —to judge from the disgraceful condition of the Mediterranean and the Adriatic—is probably worse but, as in Britain, there exists the tradition of voluntary co-operation between industry and the controlling agencies, a tradition which, certainly in Britain, is claimed to be highly successful. But only rarely is there sufficient information available to test this reassuring hypothesis. Dutch and West German authorities have, for several years, run a joint pollution monitoring station on the Rhine. The direct problem is that Holland sits at the downstream end of West Germany's effluent. Quite apart from the disaster of 1970 when pesticide spillage killed all fish life over a great length of the river, and which was publicly investigated but never resolved, the monitoring station publishes no information about river quality. As far as I know (and to return to toxic metals), no official estimates exist of the amounts of poisonous materials reaching the environment, and very few estimates of the metal burdens of single rivers or the atmospheric burdens of individual urban–industrial regions. Estimates of sulphur dioxide atmospheric burdens, and of total effluent burdens exist, but the detailed information is locked away under gentlemen's agreements to which the public has no formal access.

In the particular case of mercury losses from chlor-alkali plants, it is said (informally) by the major British producer, ICI, that 0·5 lb of mercury per ton of chlorine is about right, and there is no reason to believe that tighter operating conditions exist elsewhere in Europe. This means that, in practice, the level of control achieved by British and other European protection agencies is no better than that of the US. Since there is necessarily a much lower pressure for improvement in situations which are essentially non-public, the improvement regarded as possible by the experts at Oak Ridge is more likely to be achieved in the US where the real facts are exposed and people are prepared to shout. As it happens chlor-alkali plants may not present any serious environmental problem, for much of the lost mercury is contained and simply wasted in settling ponds. But it is symptomatic of the insensitivity of well-insulated protection systems that —with growing public concern about the seepage of toxic

wastes and about the problems of land rehabilitation—
practices of this kind continue without serious public
challenge.

The only route to an assessment of the quality of contamination control achieved by European agencies is
through the examination of the environment, and this
cannot be achieved on the basis of occasional and random
monitoring. You need a major investigation of ecological
structures, and a continuous monitoring of selected
sensitive species, particularly those with special accumulative characteristics, or those at the top of a food chain.
Major investigations are rare, because they are expensive
and because they tread on too many departmental toes.
But when environmental disasters occur public pressure
forces the machinery into action, and facts, often unpalatable facts, emerge.

Since Britain claims such great success in controlling
contamination, it is worth putting this to the test by
looking at the results of one of the few major investigations of the British environment in recent years, the
enquiry into the massive 'kill' of seabirds in the Irish Sea
in the autumn of 1969. Ornithologists estimate that in
this single incident between 50,000 and 100,000 seabirds
died, most of them guillemots[7] although razorbills and
puffins were among the 17,347 birds recorded after being
washed up on the shores of Britain. Coming after a series
of major bird kills, mainly caused by oil spillages at sea,
there was powerful public pressure for a full investigation. Under the lead of the British Natural Environment
Research Council, involving many of the major fisheries
and environmental laboratories, the various strands of
the disaster were unravelled. Yet in spite of comprehensive investigation no specific cause emerged.

Indeed it was concluded that the deaths were the result
of a combination of factors: the time of year, with the
birds weakened after the moult; a period of unusually
stormy weather for August and September, which had
made feeding difficult; the direct effects of starvation on

the ability to survive; and the mobilization of various accumulated poisons through loss of flesh. Among these poisons were high concentrations of polychlorinated-biphenyls (PCBs), the widely used industrial solvents which have been increasingly widespread as contaminants since the 1930s. PCBs behave like organochlorine pesti-cides in the environment and in living organisms, and have now been restricted in both the US and Britain *but not in Europe*.

This finding was itself disturbing and quite unexpected by ornithologists. No less unexpected, and perhaps more sinister, was the indication of high levels of contamina-tion by a whole range of toxic metals. (See Table 1.) There was no uniform distribution, but simply a scatter of findings which showed without any doubt whatever that from time to time during their lives these birds had been feeding on severely contaminated marine organisms. Cadmium, selenium, mercury, lead and several other metals were found, sometimes in concentrations which,

TABLE 1

Twelve of 18 guillemots analysed after the wreck of seabirds in the Irish Sea in the autumn of 1969 had anomalously high concentra-tions of toxic metals in their liver or kidney. This chart shows the scatter of metals found. Some of the concentrations are themselves possibly lethal. Results are expressed as ppm dry weight.

	lead	arsenic	mercury	selenium	zinc	cadmium
1.	40·0+	0·8	0·1	20·0	950·0	6·6
2.	40·0+	0·3	3·1	69·0	640·0	1·6
3.	19·0	0·1	3·7	82·0	1000·0+	12·8
4.	0·8	38·0	1·8	55·0	50·0	1·9
5.	4·9	0·3	8·0	23·0	770·0	1·4
6.	2·1	3·9	1·2	47·0	300·0+	4·3
7.	29·0	1·0	3·4	0·2	130·0	none detected
8.	7·2	0·1	5·5	414·0	170·0	12·2
9.	6·8	37·0	0·1	0·2	23·0	0·2
10.	18·0	0·1	15·0	58·0	11·0	2·5
11.	8·8	8·9	23·0	28·0	190·0	8·9
12.	3·3	9·1	0·1	19·0	30·0	11·7

CONTROL—average of four samples from healthy birds (shot).

	lead	arsenic	mercury	selenium	zinc	cadmium
	1·5	1·1	1·1	5·7*	73·3	0·27

* One bird had 16·0 ppm selenium in its kidney.

even for single metals, approached the lethal limit. One can only speculate about the combined effects of those birds found to be rich in several toxic metals.

The unexplained scatter of metals in high concentrations in the victims is an indication both of high levels of contamination and of uneven distribution in the environment. The sources of metals are unknown but the investigation suggested that, under abnormal natural stress, heavy metal poisoning was a significant contributory cause of death for upwards of 20,000 seabirds in one month in a small area of the Irish Sea. Metallic contamination appears, from this investigation alone, to be much more serious than generally believed.

One horrifying aspect of this massive bird kill is that starvation struck amid abundance. There is no indication that the foodchain itself, or the availability of normal foods, was in any way disrupted. Guillemots are largely non-migratory, so the high levels of contamination of their vital organs can be taken as an index of the extent of marine contamination off the west coast of Britain and the east coast of Ireland.

Those accustomed to the study of natural population dynamics will not be surprised that no dominant single factor could be isolated as a cause of the kill. Investigation inevitably comes after the event and natural situations are complex and full of interactions. It was as if, through a combination of different yet additive effects, the bird population went over some unseen fatal threshold beyond which normal vital forces dwindled and were no longer adequate for survival. The relevance of toxic metals and of PCBs is that one of the first effects of most kinds of poisoning is reduced appetite and reduced activity. Once started, the spiral of reduced food intake, loss of flesh, mobilization of more accumulated metallic and other poisons, and increased inability to hunt and to survive would, like the spiral dive of an aircraft, be self-perpetuating and self-intensifying.

The ragged wreckage of dead birds speaks for itself.

Like similar wildlife catastrophes in North America and elsewhere, this disaster contains a grave message whose importance cannot be overestimated. It is that the thresholds of environmental calamities are obscure; that levels of contamination are already past the point at which they can amplify many times—perhaps hundreds of times—the fatal effects of purely natural stresses; that it is impossible to predict where disasters will strike and often impossible to define causes after they have happened; and that there is little to be gained from niggling arguments about particular effects of individual components of contamination. The burdens of toxic metals as a whole, and of organochlorines, have already degraded the entire context of the life-system.

That this has happened in spite of the much vaunted British dual protection system of river authorities and the Alkali Inspectorate, leads, first, to the obvious conclusion that something is seriously wrong and, second, to the question of where the loopholes lie. Since, at the moment, we are talking principally about the western seaboard of England and Wales an appropriate place to look for clues is within the official comments of those concerned with fisheries and the marine environment in that area.

At a major conference on 'Water Pollution as a World Problem' held in Wales in 1970, a senior fisheries officer[8] pointed out that very little scientific work had been done on the ecological effects of sewage-derived solids and particulate trade wastes in coastal and estuarial waters. Then, through the question of bacterial contamination of shellfish, he pointed to a most curious and topsy-turvy state of affairs. To counteract the pollution-induced hazard of eating contaminated shellfish, many local authorities invoke the use of the Public Health (Shellfish) Regulations 1934, which allows them to prohibit the taking of shellfish from contaminated areas. (Similar procedures are common in the US.) Under these regulations, local public health authorities have progressively closed many of the productive shellfish areas along the coast. At the time of this conference fourteen areas were banned on the Lancashire, Cheshire and North Wales coasts alone.

What seems so extraordinary about this gradual invasion and destruction of coastal productivity, is that the public health authorities are concerned only with the most superficial aspect of the problem. They prevent wholesale poisoning of the human population, but neither they nor the authorities which have allowed the contamination to occur, take steps to remedy the basic cause. Fisheries are closed, fishermen are deprived of a livelihood, the public health people can say that all is well, while the malignant poisoning of the marine environment is allowed to continue and is not even properly monitored.

This insane pattern of events is typical of procedures the world over, presumably on the basis of the argument that it is cheaper to close fisheries and go on poisoning the sea than it is to clean up effluents. *Indeed the existence of public health powers to close fisheries, rather than to seek out and eliminate sources of contamination, has served over the years to condone the deterioration of the environment and to provide false reassurance when pollution matters are discussed, by pretending that actions are protective and in the interests of the public.* They are in fact in nobody's interests except those who are economically selfish and environmentally blind.

It needs to be admitted that, at this British conference, very little was said about metallic contamination, principally because nobody had looked. But the crucial disconnection between public health procedures, the activities of effluent control authorities, and the fisheries protection agencies, leaves yawning gaps through which many kinds of contaminant pour. Indeed, in 1971, Britain was still fighting against the best ecological advice of Scandinavia and northern Europe for the continuation of her growing practice of simply dumping 'difficult' industrial wastes in the North and Irish seas. Under pressure things are changing but at Government level and in spite of the establishment of a Department of the Environment, there was then still little grasp at the Foreign Office of the seriousness of present levels of contamination or of the inevitably damaging effects of continued dumping. (See note 10.) There is no longer any need to ask from where the poisons came. The seabirds died of storms and effluent, and these were metal rich. In spite of the obviously serious implications this has for the future of coastal ecology, and its reflection of the inefficiency and inadequacy of present protection techniques and policies, the signs are of an official rearguard action in Britain. It is one thing to avoid panic measures, quite another to stick your head in the effluent sediment and pretend to see no problem, and another still to initiate plausible new policies which do not really seal the gaps.

Take, for example, the new 'tough' policy of the British Government on effluent discharges into the sea from new plants. The most quoted typical example is that of Cleveland Potash Ltd in Yorkshire, set up, of all places, in a National Park, a circumstance which tells us much about the protective powers of conservation legislation in Britain. However, the notion of 'toughness' arises from the nature of the restrictions set by the Department of the Environment on the discharge of effluent. The initial permissive agreement demands a mile-long pipeline, limits on the volume of effluent, and provides for a programme of monitoring and research into the effects of discharge. The initial agreement is limited to five years and excludes compensation should evidence of damage emerge which necessitates further restrictions or even the closing of the plant. Research by the company, accepted by all the relevant authorities, has led to the conclusion that careful control can prevent damage to inshore fisheries particularly to the local shellfish industry.

It happens, in this particular instance, that the University of Leeds operates a marine research station at no great distance from the plant, a rare combination of circumstances but one which makes monitoring and ecological study possible. However, the situation is new and raises some ticklish problems. Marine biologists, all too aware of the complexity of ecosystems, are not easily persuaded to make dogmatic statements about long-term effects. Who is to say, in the end, whether changes observed in the ecology of the area—and these will certainly take place—are damaging or not? Where are the base lines to be drawn, for there are often considerable ecological changes which result from natural cycles, and these will inevitably be difficult to disentangle from the effects of effluent? *If the biological evidence reveals disturbance of the ecology but is inconclusive about damage, can some other criterion of importance to long-term effects —such as water quality—finally be taken as the baseline?*

Although it might be thought at first glance that the 'tough' policy represents a triumph for environmental common sense, it can be seen that the notion of 'suck it and see' opens up large areas of possible controversy and in fact does little more than delay the essential decision, permit the build-up of the pressures of capital commitment, and provide no clear basis on which the decision can ultimately be reached.[9] If the mile-long pipeline appears to be causing trouble, it can become a two-mile pipeline, at which length trouble may not show up for 10 years instead of five. Then, perhaps, it can become a four-mile pipeline. In the end you might just as well load the effluent onto barges and dump it far out at sea because real monitoring is impossible. It is a policy which demands that damage must be demonstrated before restrictions can be applied, and reveals all too clearly the willingness—not only of industry and Government, but of all authorities—to operate as close as possible to the borderline of ecological disaster.

But, if this potash decision is regarded as both good and tough, it is not necessarily typical of all decisions. The structure of planning permission in Britain and most

European countries operates at two levels and, unlike the US and Sweden where central protection agencies are realities, does not necessarily require the intervention of central Government or of expert authority. In Britain, as in France and Germany where the prefectures and Ländern operate, the planning authorities are local government bodies. New developments are first assessed in the light of local response and may or may not lead to a public enquiry. The strength of response depends primarily on the availability of expert knowledge and of environmental awareness in the local community. The quality of the seas are the concern of fisheries committees, but their strength and expertise varies widely, and their powers are strictly limited. Without the existence of powerful expertise in the community, crucial issues may not be raised, and European procedures do not provide for an automatic reference to higher authority. The system has the merits of convenience and speed, involves the natural rejection of bureaucracy, but fails to ensure that environmental problems receive an adequate airing.

This has a direct bearing on the build-up of toxic metals, for in many instances direct discharge of metallic residues into the sea escapes the environmental protection network by default. Further, the decision made many years ago in Britain, the US and most other advanced industrial countries, that *municipal* sewage systems should treat *industrial* wastes, has led to a large increase in the amount of metallic salts reaching the sea. Quite apart from the deleterious effect this has on prospects for re-cycling nutrient organic materials to the land—for metallic residues render poisonous otherwise valuable organic wastes—the metallic burdens of rivers have increased, as have the burdens of municipal discharges which run directly into the sea. The fishery protection agencies have no control whatever over discharges of this kind unless direct damage to fisheries can be proved. This is not a problem which will be solved by simply building more and better municipal treatment plants. It requires changes in law and the proper allocation of responsibility to industry.

The basic sewage decision, made for purely short-term industrial cost reasons, was wrong, but having been made has led to the establishment of precedents and accepted practices which will not easily be deposed. True, in West Germany and Sweden, industrial central processing plants for the specialized treatment of industrial effluents are now envisaged or in experimental use, and the pressure is growing for the elimination of all long-term poisons from residual effluents reaching the environment. Small specialized commercial plants exist in Britain and the US but initial costs are high, treatment costs are high, and national progress towards full treatment of toxic wastes is not only slow but delayed by fears of losing industrial investment. Industry, it is argued, goes to those places in which environmental protection requirements are most lax. Furthermore, laxity of protection leads to economic advantages in the market place. It seems quite incredible that such damaging, corrupt and tarnished notions should still have currency.

The toxic metals are of quite extraordinary biological potency. The very fact that you cannot put trace amounts of them back on the land with organic waste is one measure of this. Yet we cheerfully permit them to be pumped into the seas and into the atmosphere. The Baltic is dying, the Mediterranean is sick, the coastal regions of Europe and North America—including vitally productive estuaries, and the urban–industrial complexes in which most of us live—are already disrupted or seriously contaminated. The pressures, through accepted practice, through inadequate or wrongly based legislation and procedure, through complacency and through narrowly based economic assessments of the course of acceptable protective action, are all towards the continuation of old practices. The whole balance of power in the formulation of policy (in which procedural routes are predominantly non-public), lies in the hands of those dominated by notions of economic expansion and economic gain. The losses are not weighed except to determine the optimum point at which protest or gross damage will be minimized. Only the sudden disasters produce public shock, official pause and occasional action.

But the gradual deterioration, because it is gradual and therefore hard to see, goes on. To argue that, because this river or that is cleaner now than it was ten or twenty years ago, is to miss the crucial point. The basic and erroneous belief is that natural systems can always absorb and detoxify the wastes of society and its industries provided that these are adequately diluted. This assumes unlimited powers of dilution, ignores the stability and destructive potency of metals and other persistent poisons involving ever larger regions in increasing contamination, ignores reconcentration through food chains and places intolerable burdens first on city atmospheres and coastal regions, then on the global atmosphere and on the seas as a whole. Over vast areas the limits have already been approached if not reached, ecosystems are simplifying through the elimination of the more sensitive species, and instability is inevitable.

It is one of the tragedies of our time that this broad ecological argument has little force. The earth, to most of us, still seems a vast place whose natural processes are so enormous that the activities of man and his industrial civilization can have little effect on them. Yet those effects are already far-reaching and almost universally deleterious. Unless we accept the need to so organize the processes of industry and of society so that we insulate the environment from their effects then the future of mankind will be relatively short and increasingly disgusting. When the deprived and poisoned peasant fishermen of Minamata tried to smash down the gates of the plastics factory only to be beaten off and fined, they symbolized the appalling injustice, inhumanity, environmental blindness and wilful self-destruction of technological society. The acute disease of Minamata is the chronic disease of the whole world. It is not simply that the ragged litters of dead wildlife, the struggling mass of dying seabirds, the mad cats, the deformed children, the crippled rivers or the black tides of oil are the real obscenities of our time. It is that they are not *recognized* as such. They are regarded, like the cadmium and the lead in the air, as unfortunate but inevitable. Unless that view changes, and changes soon, we will be left only with a suddenly small-seeming and crippled earth and a large regret. It would be wise to ensure that the first changes embrace the toxic metals.

Notes and References

1. Royal Commission on Environmental Pollution: first report. Her Majesty's Stationery Office, February 1971, p 16.

2. See for example *Population: Resources: Environment: issues in Human Ecology* by Anne H. and Paul R. Ehrlich (Freeman, 1970), and 'Resources and Man,' American Academy of Sciences, 1969.

3. See *World Dynamics* by Jay W. Forrester (Wright-Allen Press 1971). A computer based integration of global trends.

4. 'Mercury in the Environment,' Oak Ridge National Laboratory, January 1971, pp 35–7.

5. A significant political expression of this need for change is contained in 'Science, Growth and Society: A New Perspective' prepared by an expert committee under the chairmanship of Prof. Harvey Brooks (Harvard) for the science ministerial meeting of OECD Member Countries in October 1971.

6. This point was made in the report on drinking water pollution in the United States produced by David Zwick for the US Center for the Study of Responsive Law, April 1971.

7. See 'The Seabird Wreck of 1969 in the Irish Sea,' edited by M. W. Holdgate. Natural Environment Research Council, 1971.

8. A. J. O'Sullivan: 'Water Pollution as a World Problem,' Report of a conference held at the University College of Wales, Aberystwyth (Europe Publications, July 1971).

9. These problems are discussed by J. R. Lewis in 'Reflections on a Ministerial Judgement,' *Marine Pollution Bulletin*, vol 2, No 6, June 1971.

10. International disagreement on the dumping of wastes rests largely on the definition of 'damaging'. Britain will not accept the blanket ban on waste dumping being proposed by the US and others but, through the International Maritime Consultancy Organisation (IMCO) agreement may eventually be reached. Britain favours differing controls designed to meet the requirements of particular areas—such as the North Sea, the Mediterranean, etc.

GLOSSARY

AEROBIC   microbe, or biological process involving microbes, which requires oxygen. Microbes which require oxygen are called *aerobes*.

AEROSOL   a mixture of gas and particles in which the particles are finely dispersed—like a mist—and which can therefore 'float' in the atmosphere for a long time.

ANAEROBIC   microbe, or biological process involving microbes, which can function or only function in the absence of oxygen. The opposite of aerobic.

BIODEGRADABILITY   the property, in a complex chemical compound, of breaking down into simple chemical components under the action of naturally occurring biological processes—such as those which form part of the normal life-cycle in a river or in the soil.

CARCINOGEN   any substance capable of transforming normal cells so that they become cancerous.

CARCINOGENIC   having the properties of a carcinogen.

CATALYST   substance which accelerates a chemical process without itself changing.

CHELATING AGENT   a chemical substance which, when introduced into an animal, is capable of mobilizing stored metallic poisons so that they can be excreted. Chelating agents have to be used with great care because the sudden burden of poison released by their action can damage the liver and kidneys.

DNA—DEOXYRIBONUCLEIC ACID   protein in the nucleus of living cells which contains the genetic information—the structural blueprint—of the complete organism. Small changes in the very complex structure of DNA can lead to genetic aberrations such as human genetic diseases like haemophilia, or to deformity.

ENZYME   highly specialized protein manufactured in living cells to serve as catalyst in vital chemical processes. The mode of action of enzymes is not understood, but they are very much more efficient than the metallic and other catalysts used in industry. Their activity is, however, easily disrupted.

ENZYME INTERFERENCE alteration or disruption of the bio-chemical processes in living things by inhibiting or changing the functions of a particular enzyme or enzymes. This is one of the main routes of action of metallic poisons.

ECOSYSTEM a life-structure which involves the crucial inter-dependence of many different organisms—microbes, in-sects, animals and plants—and which depends for its con-tinuance and stability on the possession of a large number of alternative conditions in which it will balance. The simplifi-cation of an ecosystem by the elimination of particular species inevitably leads to loss of stability.

ENCEPHALITIS inflammation of the brain. This can be caused by many poisons and diseases and in some instances, such as repeated lead poisoning in children, can cause irreversible and serious damage. (-itis = inflammation.)

ENCEPHALOPATHY general term for an abnormal or diseased condition of the brain. (-pathy = disease.)

EPIDEMIOLOGY the study, usually by statistical methods, of the pattern of the incidence of diseases in large populations.

FOOD CHAIN the sequence of steps from small to larger organ-isms, animals and plants, by which the food for the largest predator is created. Poisons tend to concentrate as they progress up the food chain. The human predator and other large animals are at the top, microbes are at the bottom.

GEOCHEMISTRY the study of the chemistry of the earth.

GAUSSIAN CURVE a line which, by height above a zero base, represents the number of individuals or events (in a popula-tion for example) and by distance along the horizontal represents a particular characteristic (such as height, size of feet, or blood-lead level). When a large number of measure-ments are made it is generally found that the curve is high at the centre because of the large proportion of normal and near-normal measurements, and then falls off towards either extreme to take the general outline of a Napoleonic hat.

HALF-LIFE originally used to define the length of time taken for any amount of radioactive substance to undergo the decay of half its atoms, that is to lose half of its radio-activity. Now used generally to define the residence time of any substance in a biological system, such as mercury in the brain, by the length of time it takes for half the sub-stance to be broken down or excreted.

INDUSTRIAL PLUME   the feather-shaped cloud of gas and particles which comes out of a tall chimney and is distributed by the wind. The height of the plume depends primarily on temperature relative to surrounding air at the point of exit.

METABOLIC CAPABILITY   the extent to which the natural digestive and detoxifying systems in an organism can break down and dispose of ingested compounds. This capability has been determined by evolutionary processes and is based on the naturally occurring levels of substances. Unnatural substances, such as heavy metals, cannot be metabolized—that is coped with or broken down—at a rate sufficient to protect the system or the environment.

METHYL GROUP   a chemical structure consisting of carbon and hydrogen and in the form CH_3.

METHYLIZATION   chemical process by which one or more *methyl groups* are attached to the molecule of an element, thus changing an inorganic substance to an organic substance which may have quite different biological properties.

MUTAGEN   any substance capable of increasing the rate of *mutation* of living organisms.

MUTAGENIC   having the properties of a *mutagen*.

MUTATION   the process of change in the genetic material which determines the characteristics of a species. Mutations caused by chemical compounds are generally regressive— that is they produce bizarre, grotesque or non-viable forms of the parent organism.

NEUTRON ACTIVATION ANALYSIS   analytical technique which depends on the very precise energy levels at which different elements capture and subsequently release neutrons. The substance to be analysed is first bombarded with a broad-spectrum neutron beam. The energy levels at which it subsequently releases neutrons give a very precise indication of the elements it contains.

ORGANOCHLORINE   any one of the many compounds which can be created by the chemical bonding of hydrogen and carbon atoms with chlorine. These compounds are often extremely active biologically, are very difficult to break down, and form the basis of the most potent pesticides such as DDT, Dieldrin and Aldrin.

PLUMBISM   general term describing states of poisoning induced by lead. (From *plumbum*, the Latin word for lead.)

POTENTIATING AGENT   a substance which is capable of increasing the biological activity of another substance. For example, in humans, the poisonous effects of mercury are increased by the presence of copper, and in some mammals the amount of DDT retained in the system is sharply increased if Dieldrin is taken in at the same time. In these cases copper and Dieldrin are potentiating agents.

RADIONUCLIDE a form of an element which, because of an unstable nucleus, is liable to change spontaneously and release energy. It is therefore radioactive.

RIBOSOMAL ACTIVITY the essential processes carried out in living cells by small structures called ribosomes which, acting on information transferred to them from the nuclear DNA, manufacture enzymes and other proteins for the cell.

STACK LOSSES the amount of substances either used in or produced by a process, which reach the environment by being released from an industrial chimney with (or as) hot gases.

SYNERGISM association of two or more different substances whose combined biological effect is as large as, or larger than, the sum of their separate effects. The term tends to be used most frequently to describe associations which produce biological effects *larger* than would normally be expected.

TERATOGEN a substance which, if taken by the mother, causes malformation of a developing foetus. Thalidomide, for example, although a useful drug is a powerful teratogen.

TERATOGENIC any substance having the properties of a *teratogen*.

THRESHOLD (of poisons) that level of intake which produces clinically detectable effects. This is not necessarily the level below which no damage is done.

TOXICITY the property of being poisonous or, more commonly, the degree to which a substance is poisonous. (Toxicant = poison.)

WHOLE-BODY method of measuring the overall 'insult' of either radiation or a poison which assumes an even distribution and effect throughout the system. Whole-body calculations can be seriously misleading, either because some organs are more sensitive than others or because, in the case of poisons, the amount retained differs from organ to organ.

INDEX

INDEX

air pollution: Medical Research Council Unit of, 101, 110; photochemical smog, 103

anti-knock agents, 90; amounts in petrol, 100, 107–8

antimony, 79; biological properties, 161; in sea birds, 162

arsenic, 140; cellular insult of, 200; in water, 148; synergism with lead, 163; with selenium, 162

barium, 148–9

beryllium, 165

bird kills, heavy metals in, 79, 219

brain cells, 37; damage to, 38–9

British Medical Journal: leader on mercury, 68; later leader on mercury, 196; statement on lead, 103

Bryce-Smith, Prof. D., 126

cadmium, 174–5; absorption rate, 178; and heart disease, 145–6, 180; cellular insult, 199; industrial control of, 188; in food, 185–6; in river water, 152; in tap water, 148–9, 189; in tobacco, 179; kidney damage, 182; Ouchi-Ouchi disease, 181; Severn shellfish concentrations, 155–6

Canada, 58; ban on fishing, 64

Central Unit on Environmental Pollution, 69, 123–4

cerebral cortex, 35–7

chlor-alkali industry, 80; mercury losses from, 81

cobalt, 141

concentration factors, 69

copper, 141

cyanide, 148; cellular insult, 200; in Severn estuary, 158

Danielson, Dr Lennart, 100

encephalitis, 21, 43

enzymes, 200

Epstein, Prof. S., 11–12

Federal Drug Administration, 56

foetus, 19, 60

fossil fuels: lead in, 118–19; mercury in, 83

Haley, Dr T. J., 96

hatters' madness, 31

Hospital for Sick Children, work on lead, 101

Huckleby family, mercury poisoning, 58–9

Hunter, Dr D., 33

indicator species: mosses, 167–70; pike, 50

Institute of Petroleum, 127

iodine, 138

iron, in haemoglobin, 138

Itai-Itai-Byō, *see* cadmium, Ouchi-Ouchi disease

Japan, 28, 47, 76

Jervis, Dr Robert, 58

Kehoe, Dr R. A., 97

Kumamoto University, 16, 20, 21

Lancet, The, environmental factors in disease, 139

Lead, 88–132; absorption studies, Harwell, 110; Arctic survey, 93–4; bone storage of, 98–9; calculation of intake, 114–15; cellular insult, 200; encephalitis, 97–8; human absorption, 109; in coal, 118–19; in plastic piping, 124; in river water, 153; in tap water, 120; interference in haem synthesis, 199–200; in trees, 92; major sources of, 90–1, 100, 106–7; mental health, 129; mobilization from bone, 88; 'natural' levels, 91; population levels, 90; recommended blood-lead maxima, 125; Swedish Survey, 101; US 'Five City Survey', 128

lichens, 170

Löfroth, Dr Göran, 49; on mercury threshold, 203–4

manganese, deficiency effects, 141

Massachusetts Institute of Technology, study of world trends, 210

McDuffie, Prof. B., 65

Meittinen, Prof. J. K., 73

mercury, 15–87; 'allowable' daily intake, 61–3; as catalyst, 80; effect on algae, 156–7; effect on foetus, 19; errors in 'safe' level calculation, 53–4; half-life of, 34–6; in atmosphere, 83; in eggs, 74; in hair, 76; in sea water, 71–2; in sediments, 74; methylization of, 50, 59; mutagenic effects of, 55; population effected by at Minamata, 29–30; 'safe' levels in diet, 52–3; translocation of in fruit, 54; use as seed dressing, 47; use as slimicide, 47, 74; use as syphilis treatment, 30–1

Minamata, 15–46

Minamata Disease, 15–46

molybdenum, effect on copper uptake, 141

mosses, as pollution indicators, 167–70

Nader, Ralph, 59

nephritis, 37–8

nervous system, 37–8

neutron activation analysis, 49

nickel, 191–5; carbonyls, 192–3; in fossil fuels, 193–4; in industrial wastes, 150

Niigata City, 28, 29, 30, 39, 40

Nillson, Dr Robert, 179

Oak Ridge National Laboratory, 61–2

paper-pulp industry, 51–2

Patterson, Dr C. C., 95

Penrose, Prof. L. S., 139

pica in children, 91

plastics, 25, 28; as source of lead, 124

potash, effluent control, 222–3

radiation hazards, 40–1

Reed, C. D., see Tolley, J. A.

Rhine, monitoring and pollution, 216

Rome Conference on Marine Pollution, 65, 70; recommendation, 74–5

Rosen, Dr Karl, 59

Sabrina Project, 154; metal-rich pulses in Severn, 155–6

selenium, 148; animal disease caused by, 162–3; cellular insult, 200; in Lake Michigan, 164; toxicity compared to arsenic, 162–3 shellfish, British public health regulations, 220–1

'shopping basket' surveys, 57

Standing Royal Commission on Environmental Pollution, 154

strontium-90, 41–2

sub-clinical effects, 31, 39–40, 103–4; treatment by chelating agents, 130–1

Sweden, 47–55; bird deaths in, 48; Institute of Public Health, 53; mercury information conference, 51

syphilis-treatment of, 30–1

thallium, 23

Tolley, J. A., tap water analyses, 121–2

trace-elements, 138–73; as airborne contaminants, 160; as micro-nutrients, 141–2; from petroleum, 160; Imperial College Survey, 146–7; interrelationships, 143; water survey for, 148–9

tuna, 65–6; British Government statement on, 67

United Nations: FAO, 52; WHO, 52, 55

United States: Environment Protection Agency, 69; Science Advisory Committee on Quality of the Environment, 101; Surgeon General on lead in petrol, 96, 100

vehicle pollution, 103; lead from, 88, 90, 112–13

vision, effect of mercury on, 38–9

Westöö, Prof. G., 49

White Fish Authority, oyster hatchery, 151

World Health Organization, doubling of recommended lead levels in tap water, 122

Zinc, effect on oyster larvae, 152; relationship to cadmium, 190

Environmental

Edited by John Barr, Introduction by Kenneth Allsop

THE ENVIRONMENTAL HANDBOOK:
An Action Guide to the U.K.   40p

Barry Commoner
SCIENCE AND SURVIVAL   40p

Frank Fraser Darling
WILDERNESS AND PLENTY   30p

Dr. Paul Ehrlich
THE POPULATION BOMB   30p
HOW TO BE A SURVIVOR   40p

Frank Graham Jnr
SINCE SILENT SPRING   40p

Jonathan Holliman
CONSUMERS' GUIDE TO THE
    PROTECTION OF THE
    ENVIRONMENT   40p

Farley Mowat
NEVER CRY WOLF   30p

Edited by Robert Rodale & Brian Furner
THE BASIC BOOK OF
    ORGANIC GARDENING   40p

BB

Adult Fantasy

Peter S. Beagle
THE LAST UNICORN   40p

James Cabell
CREAM OF THE JEST   40p

Lin Carter
DRAGONS, ELVES AND HEROES   40p
THE YOUNG MAGICIANS   40p

Lord Dunsany
THE KING OF ELFLAND'S
   DAUGHTER   40p
AT THE EDGE OF THE WORLD   40p

E. R. Eddison
MISTRESS OF MISTRESSES   40p
FISH DINNER AT THE MEMISON   40p
MEZENTIAN GATE   40p
THE WORM OUROBOROS   50p

BB

Adult Fantasy

David Linsay
VOYAGE TO ARCTURUS   40p

George Macdonald
LILITH   40p
PHANTASTES   40p

Hope Mirrless
LUD-IN-THE-MIST   40p

William Morris
THE WELL AT WORLD'S END
  Vol I   40p
THE WELL AT WORLD'S END
  Vol II   40p
THE WOOD BEYOND
  THE WORLD   40p
THE WATERS OF THE
  WONDROUS ISLES   40p

Evangeline Walton
ISLAND OF THE MIGHTY   40p
THE CHILDREN OF LLYR   40p

These and other PAN/BALLANTINE Books
are obtainable from all booksellers and news-
agents. If you have any difficulty please send
purchase price plus 7p postage to P.O. Box 11,
Falmouth, Cornwall.
While every effort is made to keep prices low,
it is sometimes necessary to increase prices at
short notice. PAN Books reserve the right to
show new retail prices on covers which may
differ from thise previously advertised in the
text or elsewhere.

BB